# Decimals: A Place Value Approach

LINDA A. PATRIARCA

MARILYN SCHEFFEL

SHEILA HEDEMAN

**Dale Seymour Publications**®
Orangeburg, New York

Sheila Hedeman has taught elementary school for twenty-five years in Michigan. She received her undergraduate and her graduate degree from Michigan State University. She lives in Okemos, Michigan with her son Brad.

Linda Patriarca is a professor in the Department of Counseling, Educational Psychology and Special Education at Michigan State University. She began her career in education as a public school special education teacher. Today, in the graduate program, Dr. Patriarca teaches a course on teaching mathematics to students who have mild impairments. The contents of this book grew out of a research project which was directed by Dr. Patriarca.

Marilyn Scheffel has taught special education for twenty-five years. Her BA and MA degrees in special education are from Michigan State University. She has worked with juvenile delinquents in a training school setting, young high-risk kindergarten age children in a federal project, and most recently has been a resource teacher for kindergarten through high school. She lives in East Lansing, Michigan with her husband and daughter.

Published by Dale Seymour Publications®, an imprint of
Addison Wesley Longman, Inc.

Dale Seymour Publications
125 Greenbush Road South
Orangeburg, NY 10962
Customer Service: 800-872-1100

Managing Editor: Catherine Anderson
Project Editor: Kim Thoman/John Nelson
Production/Manufacturing Director: Janet Yearian
Production Coordinator: Alan Noyes/Fiona Santioanni
Design Manager: Jeff Kelly
Illustrations: Leslie Dunlap
Text Design: Andrew Ogus

Order number 21414
ISBN 0–86651–958–0

1 2 3 4 5 6 7 8 9 ML 02 01 00 99 98 97

This Book Is Printed
On Recycled Paper

# CONTENTS

## UNIT FOUR

# Understanding the Written Algorithm    36

## UNIT FIVE

# Regrouping with Large Numbers    44

## UNIT SIX

# Decimal Fractions: Tenths    56

## UNIT SEVEN

# Decimal Fractions: Hundredths    64

# ACKNOWLEDGMENTS

As we complete this book, we wish to acknowledge those who have contributed so much to this effort.

First, all of us wish to express our deepest and most heartfelt thanks to Dolly Schmidt, who served us both as a field reader and technical editor. Not only did she format the manuscript on disk but spent countless hours reading and editing the text. Her efforts were truly a labor of love, and without her, this book may never have been published.

Next, each of us wishes to thank our families for their love, support, patience, and encouragement.

I (Linda Patriarca) want to acknowledge my husband, Donald E. Holbrook, Jr. His belief in my abilities gave me the strength to tackle this project, and his understanding and support gave me the encouragement to see it through.

I (Marilyn Scheffel) want to thank my husband, Steve, for his support and my daughter, Elizabeth, for her assistance in composing and reviewing some of the story problems in this book.

I (Sheila Hedeman) want to express my gratitude to Brad, my son, who was so patient with my absences every weekend to write this book.

We wish to thank the Okemos School District for their cooperation and support in conducting two consecutive summer school programs for students with special needs. We must also thank the teachers and graduate students who worked with us in the program. They field-tested many of the activities which found their way into this book.

Last, but not least, we must thank the youngsters at Kinawa Middle School who attended the summer school programs. They taught us so much about teaching rational numbers, and to them we owe a special debt of gratitude.

# INTRODUCTION

## Purpose of this Book

This book is designed to provide general education and special education teachers with a guided sequence for teaching decimal concepts and relating them to place value. Our objective is to help teachers provide students with an understanding of decimals as an extension of the place value system. We want students to recognize the fundamental relationship between place value in whole numbers and decimals. Consequently, this book begins with instruction in whole number place value and reiterates this organizing principle throughout the text. This approach is to make clear the powers of ten continuum governing place value.

This text provides a model for teaching troublesome content with an in-depth, step-by-step approach to instruction. It demonstrates how to foster connections between mathematical ideas such as tenths and hundredths and how to use concrete materials to help students visualize these mathematical ideas.

## Target Learners

Although this text was originally written to provide instruction for middle school students who were learning disabled or academically at-risk, it has been used successfully with fifth and sixth grade students and with high school students in basic mathematics classes. In addition, the beginning units on whole numbers have been used with third and fourth graders with success. These units could serve as a review for students who understand the base ten system or as remedial instruction for others.

## Key Features of this Book

- **Provides a sequential teaching model that demonstrates the relationship between place value and the decimal system**

This book follows a general sequence of instruction to teach the concepts of tenths, hundredths, and thousandths. First, the concept is introduced. Next, experiences in comparing and ordering quantities with multiple representations is introduced using a place value chart as the cornerstone. Finally, students extend and apply knowledge through computation and application activities.

- **Provides an instructional model that uses multiple representations to express mathematical concepts**

In each unit of study, Lesh's model[1] is used as a framework for constructing tasks and activities. Multiple modes—pictures, manipulatives, written symbols, and spoken symbols—help students grasp the abstract mathematical ideas. For example, students are asked to write the decimal and then to shade in the equivalent amount on a picture or to construct the quantity on a place value chart and then shade in the equivalent amount on a counting square. Retaining and applying mathematical learning depends on the student's abilities to move effortlessly between different mathematical modes.

- **Provides teachers with scripted scenarios as models for how to teach the content and assess student understanding**

In order to provide teachers with the most detailed information about how to teach decimal concepts and assess student learning, the text includes scripted scenarios to describe the general sequence of activities.

- **Provides teachers with specific examples of how to infuse assessment into instruction**

A unique feature, *Assessment Opportunities,* is included at the end of each unit. This section describes the formal and informal evaluation measures contained within the unit and presents techniques for determining student understanding. The role of the assessment, emphasized throughout the text, is to inform and direct the pace of instruction rather than to grade students.


## Organization of this Book

This book starts with the review of whole number place value and concludes with real-world problems that incorporate addition and subtraction of decimals to the thousandths place. The first page of each unit lists the materials required for that unit. The blackline masters, used to make worksheets, manipulatives and transparencies, are provided at the rear of the book.

Each of the units contains a series of instructional sequences designed to introduce the concepts, compare/order quantities, and apply conceptual understanding through problem-solving activities. The instructional sequences are presented to help teachers adjust the pace of instruction depending on their perceptions of student needs.

Following the instructional sequences, every unit has a section entitled *Reinforcement Activities.* This section provides a number of activities teachers can use

[1]Post, T.R., ed. "Some Notes on the Nature of Mathematical Learning," *Teaching Mathematics in Grades K–8: Research-Based Methods.* (2nd ed.), p. 13, Allyn & Bacon, Needham Heights, Mass.

to reinforce the concepts and skills taught in the unit. Students work independently, with partners and in small groups playing games and solving real-world problems.

The final section of each unit, *Assessment Opportunities,* emphasizes the integrative nature of assessment and instruction by focusing on the multiple assessment opportunities contained within each instructional sequence. Reinforcement activities that are particularly well suited to assessment are identified.

## Teaching Approach

Several philosophical tenets and instructional principles guided the development of the units:

- **Student understanding develops from the experience of visualizing mathematical concepts in different ways. Pictures, manipulatives, written symbols, spoken symbols, and real-world problems are used to construct tasks and help students grasp the mathematical idea.**

- **Dialogue within groups and between the teacher and students is crucial to learning mathematics. Discussion is focused on explaining, predicting, thinking aloud, and demonstrating understanding.**

- **Establishing a community of learners is an essential ingredient in successful mathematics learning. Thus, each unit contains numerous activities which provide students with frequent opportunities to work together in various configurations (pairs, triads, teams).**

- **An essential role of assessment is to guide future instruction. Assessment must be multi-faceted, allowing students many different ways to demonstrate their understanding, yet at the same time be straightforward, simple, and integrated into daily instruction.**

# PREPARATION

The Desktop Place Value Chart and the Digit Place Value Chart are important components used throughout this text. Before beginning instruction, make a desktop place value chart for each student or pair and a digit place value chart for the front of the room.

## How to Make a Desktop Place Value Chart

Materials

■ Poster board (color a)          1 piece, 11" x 16"

■ Poster board (color b)          1 piece, 11" x 12"

■ Black marking pen

■ Masking tape

Step 1          Tape together the two 11" sides of the poster boards to form a hinge. (Note: for the first five units, students fold the decimal section underneath and use only the whole number section.)

Step 2          Draw a horizontal guideline across the whole chart a few inches from the bottom.

Step 3          Draw vertical lines 4" apart across the chart to make 7 places.

Step 4          Label each place below the horizontal line, from left to right, with a place value number (1,000 to .001) and name (thousands to thousandths).

Step 5          Draw a decimal point on the horizontal line in the left hand corner of the tenths place.

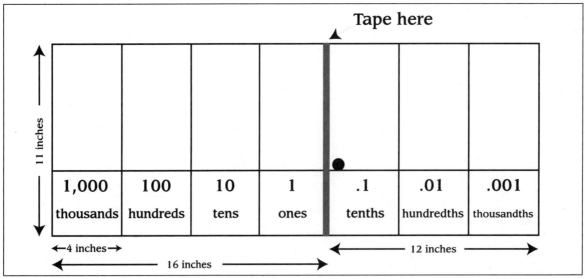

# How to Make a Digit Place Value Chart

Materials

- Poster board (color a)        4 pieces, 11" x 22"
- Poster board (color b)        3 pieces, 11" x 22"
- Poster board (color c)        3 pieces, 11" x 22"
- Transparent acetate           10 pieces, 2" x 4"
- Index cards                   100 cards, 3" x 5"
- Black marking pen
- Masking tape
- Clear tape

Step 1        Tape together all of the poster board pieces along the 22" sides. Alternate colors to make the places create an "abc" pattern.

Step 2        Lightly draw a horizontal guideline across the whole chart a few inches from the bottom to locate where to tape the transparent pockets.

Step 3        Tape pieces of acetate (lengthwise) in the middle of each place along the guideline to form pockets.

Step 4        Label each place above the pockets with a place value name (millions to thousandths).

Step 5        Draw a decimal point on the horizontal guideline in the left-hand corner of the tenths place.

Step 6        Below the horizontal guideline write "Whole Number Places" and "Decimal Places."

Step 7        Make 10 sets of digit cards (0 to 9) that are easily placed in the acetate pockets and clearly read from the back of the classroom.

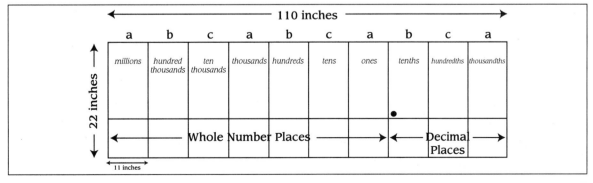

# UNIT ONE

# REVIEW WHOLE NUMBER PLACE VALUE

## Purpose of Unit

To review the whole number place value system and introduce the essential materials that will be used throughout this manual.

## Key Concepts

In the place value system, the position of a digit represents its value. The base-ten place value system is organized by grouping and trading collections of ten.

## Blackline Masters

- Assessment 1A: Whole Numbers

- Assessment 1B: Whole Numbers Applications

- Manipulatives 1A: Large Counting Squares

- Manipulatives 1B: Small Counting Squares

- Worksheet 1A: Show Your Age

- Worksheet 1B: Value of Digits

## Other Materials

- Desktop place value charts (See Preparation section on page x.)

- Overhead projector

- Paper clips

- Rubber bands

# Part I

# Place Value/Whole Number Pretests

*Administer assessments.*

Before initiating instruction, administer *Assessment 1A: Whole Numbers* and *Assessment 1B: Whole Numbers Applications.*

# Part II

# Meaning of Place Value

*Give a brief history of the Hindu-Arabic number system.*

Tell the students that in the next few weeks they'll be learning about decimals. Explain that before they begin the unit on decimals, you need to make sure they have a good understanding of the number system.

> Our number system originally came from India several centuries ago and was modified in Arabia, which is why we call the numbers Arabic numbers. Just as the twenty-six letter alphabet symbolizes every sound in the English language, the digits in the base-ten system represent all possible numbers.

■ What are the digits in our number system?

*(0 through 9)*

■ How many digits is that?

*(10)*

■ Is there a number we can't build using these 10 digits?

*(no)*

■ Can you think of a number system that doesn't use these digits?

*(Roman numerals)*

> In the Roman Numeral system, letters are used to represent amounts. (I = 1; V = 5; X = 10; L = 50; C = 100; M = 1000) This system uses addition and subtraction to represent an individual number. For example, 9 is written IX to stand for 10 − 1. And 28 is written XXVIII, which stands for 10 + 10 + 5 + 1 + 1 + 1.

Point out to students that the numbers in the Roman numeral system become very long and cumbersome to write and to compute.

## *Discuss how the position of a digit determines its value.*

Tell students the base-ten number system relies on an efficient organizing principle—place value. Each digit's value is determined by its position in the number. Write the number 23 on the overhead.

- **In the number 23, what does the 2 represent?**

   *(2 groups of 10 ones or 2 tens)*

- **What does the 3 represent?**

   *(3 ones)*

- **Suppose we reversed the digits so that the number was 32. What would the 3 represent?**

   *(3 groups of 10 ones or 3 tens)*

Point out that when the position of the 3 in the number is changed, its value is also changed. Continue with more examples.

# Part III

# Regrouping Counting Squares

## *Introduce the four different kinds of counting squares.*

Use *Manipulatives 1A: Large Counting Squares* or *Manipulatives 1B: Small Counting Squares* to make the counting squares that students use throughout this text. (Beginning with decimals in Unit Six, however, we recommend that only the Large Counting Squares are used.) You will need at least 250 counting squares per student. If you are a special education teacher working with small groups of students, you may wish to use the larger counting squares throughout the text because they are easier to manipulate. If you are a general education teacher, you may prefer to use the small counting squares until you begin Unit Six. The smaller squares require a bit more than one ream of paper for 24 students.

Each counting square, regardless of how it is divided, has the value of *one*. It is important, however, that the students use all of the different counting squares (regardless of whether they are divided into tenths, hundredths, thousandths, or are solid) interchangeably as they begin exploring whole numbers. Doing this provides an essential preparation for creating the bridge between whole numbers and decimals.

In exploring whole numbers, students will count the *ones,* paper clip them into *tens,* rubber band them into *hundreds,* and bag them into *thousands.* Later, beginning in Unit Six, students will cut up the counting squares to construct decimals.

> **We are going to use counting squares to help us understand whole number place value. Here are all four different kinds of counting squares.**

■ **Can anyone tell me in what way they are the same?**

*(all the same size, all square, all white, etc.)*

■ **How are they different?**

*(one is blank, another is divided into 10 equal parts, another is divided into 100 equal parts, and another is divided into 1,000 equal parts)*

**All of our counting squares are the same size and, despite how they are divided by lines, each has the value of one.**

## Demonstrate the regrouping process.

Continue from the previous segment. Have students count nine squares, out loud, to make a one-to-one correspondence.

■ **What happens when I add one more?**

*(you have 10)*

**I am going to paper clip this group of 10 ones.**

■ **Whenever you see a paper-clipped packet of counting squares, what does it represent?**

*(it represents 1 group of 10 ones, or 1 ten)*

Hold up 1 clipped ten and 1 one.

■ **Then if I have one more counting square, what number have I constructed?**

*(11, or 1 ten and 1 one)*

**Write the number 11 on the chalkboard and point to the tens place.**

■ **What does this 1 stand for?**

*(students identify the clipped ten)*

Point to the ones place.

■ **What does this 1 stand for?**

*(students identify the single counting square)*

■ **Who can help me count out nine more counting squares?**

*(students help)*

■ **What shall we do with our ones now?**

*(clip them into a ten)*

■ **What do we have now?**

*(20, or 2 tens)*

■ **What if we add 11 to our 20? What would we have then?**

*(31, or 3 tens and 1 one)*

Continue counting and regrouping counting squares, as needed.

# Part IV

# Constructing Numbers on the Place Value Chart

*Introduce the desktop place value chart and build numbers to 100.*

Introduce the desktop place value charts to students and distribute counting squares. Ask students to look at their place value chart and notice that it is made into two sections and can be folded over.

> This chart shows place value positions from *thousandths*, a decimal number, to *thousands*, a whole number. I would like you to fold your chart so only the whole numbers show.

Explain to the students that when they construct numbers, they put the clipped packets of tens in the tens place and all single ones in the ones place.

> Let's build the number 34 on our charts. Remember we clip only when we have a packet of tens.

■ How many clipped packets of ten are there in 34?

*(3)*

■ How many loose ones in the ones place?

*(4)*

■ Count all of the counting squares used to construct 34. How many are there?

*(34; 3 tens and 4 ones, or 34 ones)*

■ Let's build the number 58. How many tens will that be?

*(5)*

■ How many ones go in the ones place?

*(8)*

■ Count all of the counting squares used to construct 58. How many are there?

*(58; 5 tens and 8 ones, or 58 ones)*

Continue asking the same kind of questions while students construct other numbers. Each time discuss the various ways the number can be described.

> Let's build 90.

■ Now that we have 90 built, let's add 10.

*(students do it)*

■ What number have we constructed?

*(100)*

- **Is there another way to express that number?**

   *(10 tens, or 100 ones)*

   When you had 10 ones, you clipped them together into 1 group of ten. When you have 10 tens, you will put a rubber band around them to show that they are 1 group of a hundred.

- **1 ten equals how many ones?**

   *(10)*

- **1 hundred equals how many tens?**

   *(10)*

- **How many ones in 1 hundred?**

   *(100)*

- **Now that we have built a hundred, where should it go on the place value chart?**

   *(put it above the word hundreds)*

- **Are there extra tens in the tens place, or ones in the ones place now?**

   *(no, they have been regrouped to form 1 hundred)*

Write the number 100 on the chalkboard. Underline the 0 in the ones place and point out that means there are no ones. Underline the 0 in the tens place and point out that means there are no tens. Underline the 1 in the hundreds place and point out that means there is 1 hundred.

   Give students additional numbers to build. Observe how students are regrouping and trading their counting squares and ask them to explain their process.

# Part V

# Reinforcement Activities

## Activity 1: Show Your Age

Organize students in pairs. Distribute to each pair approximately 200 counting squares, a desktop place value chart and *Worksheet 1A: Show Your Age*.

   Ask students to build numbers using their counting squares to represent and combine their ages and those of their relatives.

## *Activity 2: Value of Digits*

Organize students to work in pairs or individually. Distribute a copy of *Worksheet 1B: Value of Digits.* Have students answer the questions. Then, either collect the worksheets and evaluate them or have students discuss their responses in a large group.

# Part VI

# Assessment Opportunities

There are several opportunities for assessment in this first unit. First, the pretests on whole number place value provide a sweeping general assessment of students' present levels of performance and understanding. Second, the worksheets designed to accompany Reinforcement Activities 1 and 2 can serve as unit-based assessments.

# GROUPING AND TRADING: THREE PLACES

## Purpose of Unit

To illustrate with counting squares the grouping and trading rules inherent in the place value system.

## Key Concepts

The base-ten place value system is organized and consistent in its regrouping and trading procedures.

## Blackline Masters

- Worksheet 2A: Catalogue Shopping

- Worksheet 2B: Flexible Regrouping

- Worksheet 2C: Numbers Out of Sequence

## Other Materials

- Counting squares

- Desktop place value charts

- Overhead projector

- Paper clips

- Rubber bands

# Part I

# Regrouping and Looking for Patterns

*Review the concept and process of regrouping.*

Distribute a desktop place value chart and a minimum of 125 counting squares to each student. Review with the students the value of the counting squares.

**Here is a counting square.**

■ **What is its value?**

*(1)*

**Here is a different one.**

■ **What is its value?**

*(1)*

**Here are all the 4 different kinds.**

■ **Are each of the counting squares the same amount?**

*(yes)*

■ **Even though the squares all look different, are they each the same amount?**

*(yes)*

■ **Put 9 counting squares on your place value chart.**

*(students do it)*

■ **Now, add one more square.**

*(students do it)*

■ **What happens when we add 1 more counting square to our 9 ones?**

*(we have 10)*

Make a table on the board or overhead with columns for hundreds, tens, and ones. Then construct 1 ten by clipping 10 ones together.

**A number can be written to symbolize this group of 10 ones.**

■ **Can someone show us how to write the number 10, which symbolizes this group of 10 ones, on this table?**

*(student writes 1 in the tens place and 0 in the ones place)*

Make sure the students understand that the *1* in the tens place stands for *1 group of ten* and the *0* in the ones place represents *0 ones in the number*. Repeat the process of constructing two-digit numbers with counting squares and have various student volunteers write the numbers on the table.

Continue by collecting 9 tens from the students. Then add 9 more ones.

■ **Who can tell me what number this is?**

*(99)*

■ **How would we write this number on our table?**

*(student writes the number 99 on the table)*

Have students construct 99 on their desktop place value charts and then ask them to add 1 more one. Observe students to determine whether they recognize that regrouping is required.

■ **When we added 1 more one to our 9 ones what happened?**

*(we made another group of 10)*

■ **Can we leave that group of 10 in the ones place?**

*(no)*

■ **What should we do with our new group of 10?**

*(put it in the tens place)*

■ **Now, how many tens do we have?**

*(10)*

■ **What do you think we should do with our group of 10 tens?**

*(group 10 tens into 1 hundred)*

■ **Who can write that number on our table?**

*(student writes 100)*

Repeat the process of adding 1 to other numbers, such as: 129, 149, 199, 219. Have the students work in pairs. While the students count and regroup the counting squares, observe and note difficulties.

## Students identify and describe patterns in regrouping.

Continue from the previous segment. After students have constructed several numbers, ask probing questions to determine if they are finding patterns.

■ **When we have 9 in the ones place and add 1 more one, what do we do?**

*(regroup 10 ones to make 1 ten)*

■ **When we have 9 in the tens place and add 1 more ten, what do we do?**

*(regroup the 10 tens to make 1 hundred)*

■ **What would happen if we had the number 190, and added 1 more ten?**

*(the 10 tens would make 1 hundred and now we would have 2 hundreds)*

Have students prove their answer by constructing and then regrouping on their place value charts. Reinforce the concept of regrouping on the tens and hundreds place by using larger numbers. You may need to distribute additional counting squares in order to repeat the process with more three-digit numbers.

# Part II

# Adding Prices Requiring Regrouping

*Students construct and combine prices using counting squares.*

Organize the students into groups of three. Each group should have at least 325 counting squares. Designate each student in the group as an A, B, or C. Be sure that students have paper, pencils, and desktop place value charts. Write the following information on the chalkboard or overhead:

| | | |
|---|---|---|
| Students A: | Boom Box | $139 |
| Students B: | Dirt Bike | $111 |
| Students C: | Jeans | $ 51 |

Ask students to construct the cost of their item on their place value chart. Once students have constructed the cost, tell them each group is going to combine the costs of all three items on a single place value chart. Guide the students through the process.

> **Combine the ones in the A and B prices. Next, combine the tens and hundreds in the A and B prices.**

Have students write the total of A and B prices on a piece of paper. Ask the students if they needed to regroup. Then continue.

> **Combine the ones in the C price to the total ones of A and B. Finally, combine the tens and hundreds in the C price with the total tens and hundreds of A and B.**

Discuss the answer and then give groups more problems involving the purchase of consumer goods.

# Part III

# Developing Flexibility in Regrouping

*Students build and rename numbers in multiple ways.*

Distribute 250 counting squares and desktop place value charts. Tell the students an item costs $129, and ask them to build the number on their place value charts.

- ■ **How many hundreds are in that number?**

  *(1)*

- ■ **How many tens?**

  *(2)*

- ■ **How many ones?**

  *(9)*

  **Let's look at this number in a another way. Build it again, but this time use only tens and ones.**

When they are finished, ask students how many tens are in the number. Students might say that there are 2 tens (if they are looking at the number $129). You should acknowledge that there is a 2 in the tens place in the number, but emphasize that you want to know *how many tens are in the entire number.*

- ■ **How many tens do we have altogether?**

  *(12 tens)*

- ■ **How can we prove that there are 12 tens in the number 129?**

  *(volunteer counts the clipped groups)*

  **We can think of the number 129 in different ways. We can think of it as 1 hundred, 2 tens, and 9 ones. Or, we can think of it as 12 tens and 9 ones.**

Then ask the students how many ones would they have if they didn't clip their counting squares into tens. Students might say 9 ones (if they are looking at the number $129). Again, acknowledge the 9 ones, but emphasize that you want them to *identify how many ones are in the entire number.*

- ■ **How many ones do we have altogether?**

  *(129)*

- ■ **How can we prove that there are 129 ones?**

  *(count them)*

  **We can think of the number 129 as 1 hundred, 2 tens, and 9 ones. Or we can think of it as 12 tens and 9 ones. Or we can think of it as 129 ones.**

> *Repeated experiences counting, regrouping, trading and renaming help students connect digit value to position and internalize the rules inherent in the place value system.*

Repeat the process above with several different numbers, such as 233, 69, 108, 70.

# Part IV

# Flexible Regrouping: Digit Values Out of Sequence

### *Students order, build, and write numbers.*

Distribute 250 counting squares and place value charts. Tell the students that you are going to give them numbers to build. Explain that the ones, tens, and hundreds will be out of order.

**Group your counting squares to show 9 tens, 1 hundred, and 7 ones. Then put them on your place value chart where they belong.**

Ask volunteers to share with the class how they reordered it. Then ask the students to write the number using digits (197).

**Let's repeat this process of ordering, building, and writing with the following number values:**

| 6 ones | 4 tens | 2 hundreds |
|---|---|---|
| 5 tens | 3 ones | 2 hundreds |
| 9 ones | 0 hundreds | 8 tens |
| 2 hundreds | 4 ones | 0 tens |
| 6 ones | 1 ten | 0 hundreds |

■ **Did we have to reorder all of them?**

*(yes)*

■ **Did we also have to regroup and trade?**

*(no, just reorder)*

### *Students reorder and build numbers requiring regrouping.*

Explain to the students they're going to continue building numbers that are out of order. Tell them the numbers may be a little harder, however, because they may have to be regrouped as well as reordered.

Let's build these numbers on our place value charts: 11 tens, 5 ones, and 1 hundred.

Encourage students to talk with each other about what they should do. Continue after students finish building the number.

Let's talk about how we did it.

■ **What did we do with our ones?**

*(put them in the ones place)*

■ **What did we do with our tens?**

*(left 1 ten in the tens place)*

■ **But we had 11 tens! Is it possible to have 11 tens in the tens place?**

*(no)*

■ **What must we do?**

*(put a rubber-band around 10 of the tens to make 1 hundred and put it in the hundreds place)*

■ **Now, how many hundreds do we have?**

*(2)*

■ **Who can read and write the number?**

*(student does it)*

Let's repeat this process with the following amounts:

| | | |
|---|---|---|
| 15 ones | 9 tens | 2 hundreds |
| 0 hundreds | 13 ones | 12 tens |
| 1 hundred | 29 ones | 0 tens |
| 5 ones | 15 tens | 1 hundred |
| 19 tens | 18 ones | 2 hundreds |

# Part V

# Reinforcement Activities

## Activity 1: Catalogue Shopping

Organize students to work in pairs. Distribute 300 counting squares, a place value chart, and a copy of *Worksheet 2A: Catalogue Shopping* to each pair. Have students work together to build the numbers on the place value chart with the counting squares. Have both students put their names on the worksheet and complete it together.

## Activity 2: Flexible Regrouping

Organize students to work in pairs. Distribute 300 counting squares, a place value chart, and a copy of *Worksheet 2B: Flexible Regrouping* to each pair. Both students are to put their names on the worksheet and complete it together. Have one student build the numbers using the place value chart and counting squares. Have the other reorder and regroup the numbers, in writing, on the worksheet.

## Activity 3: Numbers Out of Sequence

Give each student 300 counting squares, a place value chart, and *Worksheet 2C: Numbers Out of Sequence.* Ask the students to build the number using their counting squares and record the number on the worksheet. Identify students who may need some small group instruction. Take the opportunity to form a small group and help them reorder and build numbers.

# Part VI

# Assessment Opportunities

The reinforcement activities in this unit can be used for review or as formal assessments. *Worksheet 2C: Numbers Out of Sequence* can be used as a curriculum-based assessment. If students miss numbers 1 through 5, teach Part III again. If students miss numbers 6 through 9, teach Part IV again.

There are also several informal assessment opportunities. Observe students as they build numbers on the place value charts using the counting squares and ask questions to informally assess their understanding. Another rich opportunity to assess understanding occurs while observing students working in small, cooperative groups counting, combining and regrouping manipulatives to represent catalogue items. Building out-of-sequence numbers offers yet another instance to evaluate whether students are grasping the concept or are becoming confused.

# UNIT THREE

# ADDITION AND SUBTRACTION: THREE PLACES

## Purpose of Unit

To reinforce the grouping and trading rules of the base-ten place value system and apply these rules in addition and subtraction.

## Key Concepts

The base-ten place value system of regrouping involves "putting together" and "breaking up" various collections of ten. Patterns underlie all mathematics.

## Blackline Masters

- Manipulatives 3A: Digit Cards

- Worksheet 3A: Addition Recording Sheet

- Worksheet 3B: Patterns of Five Ledger (also make a transparency)

- Worksheet 3C: Subtraction Recording Sheet

- Worksheet 3D: Addition and Subtraction Recording Sheet

- Worksheet 3E: Shopping List Problems

## Other Materials

- Counting squares

- Desktop place value charts

- Digit place value chart and digit cards (See Preparation section on page xi.)

- Overhead projector

- Paper clips

- Playing cards

- Rubber bands

- Scissors

# Part I

# Regrouping on the Place Value Chart

### *Students build, reorder, and regroup numbers.*

Distribute desktop place value charts, 200 counting squares, paper clips, and rubber bands to each student. Then introduce students to the digit place value chart and discuss how it is the same and different from their desktop place value chart.

> **Build a number, on your desktop chart, that is made up of 7 ones and 3 tens.**

While students are working, show the number 37 on the digit place value chart using digit cards.

- **What is that number?**

  *(37)*

> **Build a number, on your charts, that is made up of 1 ten and 19 ones. But, for now, just put the 19 ones in the ones place.**

While students are working show the number 29 on the digit chart.

- **Using what we've learned about groups of ten, who would like to tell us what we should do with the 19 ones?**

  *(we take 10 of the 19 ones and make one group of 10, which we put in the tens place)*

Encourage students to explain the process, but don't become dismayed if they have not developed a fully functioning mathematical language to communicate their ideas. Assist and clarify if needed. Be sure that all students regroup the ones on their place value charts to make 2 tens and 9 ones before proceeding.

- **What number have we built?**

  *(29)*

- **Do you think that 1 ten and 19 ones equals 2 tens and 9 ones?**

  *(yes)*

- **Do you think that 1 ten and 19 ones equals 29 ones?**

  *(yes)*

> **Let's build a number that is made up of 11 tens and 13 ones on our charts.**

While students are working show the number 123 on the digit chart. Then observe the students while they build the number to see whether they recognize the need to regroup in both the ones and tens places. If not, guide them through the regrouping procedure. Encourage students to verbalize what they did and why.

- **What number have we built?**

  *(123)*

Review the regrouping process.

- **What do we call this process?**

  *(regrouping)*

  **Build a number that is made up of 1 ten and 25 ones on your chart.**

While the students are working, show the number 35 on the digit chart.

- **What is that number?**

  *(35)*

- **How can we prove our answer?**

  *(student answers will vary)*

- **Build a number that is made up of 12 tens and 0 ones.**

While students are working, show the number 120 on the digit chart.

- **What number did we build?**

  *(120)*

- **How can we prove it?**

  *(answers vary)*

Have students continue building several other numbers. Each time make the number on the digit chart with the digit cards and have the students prove their answer.

## Students build and record numbers.

Ahead of time, clip and rubber band counting squares into several hundreds and about 20 tens. Have the digit place value chart available.

Hold up 11 tens and 15 ones. Ask for a volunteer to come to the front of the class and regroup the counting squares. Have the student show the number with digits on the chart.

Do more examples with other volunteers. You might use: 9 tens and 19 ones; 17 tens and 3 ones; 1 hundred, 3 tens and 19 ones. Have students move back and forth between the manipulative representation of counting squares and the written symbols of the digit cards.

# Part II

# Addition on the Place Value Chart

## Students add by 5s by building and recording algorithms.

Organize students into pairs. Distribute to each pair a place value chart, 200 counting squares, paper clips, rubber bands, and *Worksheet 3A: Addition Recording Sheet.*

Tell the students they are going to add numbers on the place value chart using what they've been learning about counting and regrouping.

One person in each pair will be a builder and one person will be a recorder.

■ **Look at the first problem on the worksheet. Recorders, who can read it?**

*(student reads 0 + 0 = 0)*

■ **Look at the second problem. Recorders, who can read it?**

*(student reads 0 + 5 = 5)*

■ **Builders, how can we build this problem on the place value chart?**

*(put 5 ones on the chart)*

Explain to the recorders they are to use the answers from each previous problem to make the next problem by writing in the boxes. They are adding by 5s.

■ **Now, what is our third problem?**

*(5 + 5)*

■ **Builders, how can we build this problem?**

*(put 5 more ones on the chart)*

■ **What is our total?**

*(10 ones)*

■ **What do we have to do?**

*(paper clip them to make 1 ten)*

■ **Recorders, how did we write that on our sheet?**

*(with a 1 and 0, or 10)*

■ **Recorders, what is our fourth problem?**

*(10 + 5)*

■ **Builders, how can we build it?**

*(put another 5 ones on the chart)*

■ **What is the answer?**

*(15)*

■ **Recorders, what should we be doing?**

*(writing the answer 15 on the recording sheet)*

■ **Did we have to regroup?**

*(no)*

■ **Recorders, what is our fifth problem?**

*(15 + 5)*

■ **Builders, how can we build it?**

*(put another 5 ones on the chart)*

- **What else do we have to do?**

  *(regroup the 10 ones into 1 ten)*

- **Recorders, what have we recorded?**

  *(20)*

- **Did we have to regroup also?**

  *(yes)*

- **How did we write that on our sheet?**

  *(with a 2 and a 0, or 20)*

- **Would a volunteer write the number on the chalkboard?**

  *(student writes 20)*

- **Would a volunteer make the number on our digit place value chart?**

  *(student does it)*

- **How many ones does that number represent?**

  *(20)*

- **What else can we call that?**

  *(2 tens)*

Have the students continue the process of adding 5 at a time, building and recording. Encourage students to change roles when they reach 60. Explain to the students that when they regroup numbers in addition, it is the same process as paper clipping the counting squares into tens, or banding them into hundreds.

> **When we carry whole numbers in addition, we're not just carrying a 1 or a 2, but we're carrying tens, hundreds and so on. You can see why the word *regroup* is used. It reminds us that we're making collections of ten.**

## Students discover patterns.

Students need their completed Worksheet 3A: Addition Recording Sheet. Have available copies of *Worksheet 3B: Patterns of Five Ledger* and a transparency of it.

Review the completed Worksheet 3A with the students. Encourage them to explain when they regrouped.

Distribute copies of Worksheet 3B to the students and put a transparency of it on the overhead.

> **Let's record the answers of our addition problems on this worksheet called a ledger. We'll also write how many ones, tens, and hundreds are in each answer.**

After completing the ledger, ask students if they see any patterns.

- **What pattern do you see in the ones place?**

  *(0, 5, 0, 5, 0, 5)*

■ **What pattern do you see in the tens place?**

*(0, 0, 1, 1, 2, 2, 3, 3)*

---

*Patterns underlie all mathematics. The discovery of patterns expands the student's overall number sense and promotes logical thinking, a critical element in successful mathematics learning.*

---

# Part III

# Subtraction on the Place Value Chart

## Students subtract by building and recording the algorithms.

Organize students into pairs. Distribute to each pair a place value chart, 200 counting squares, paper clips, rubber bands, and *Worksheet 3C: Subtraction Recording Sheet*. The digit place value chart should be in view.

Explain to the students that regrouping not only occurs in addition, but also in subtraction.

> **We've been adding and then regrouping on our place value charts. We need to also regroup when we do subtraction. You and your partner will investigate how that works. One of you will be a builder and the other a recorder.**

Have builders construct 120 on their place value charts with their counting squares. Check students' work to ensure that everyone does this successfully.

■ **What did you put on your chart to make 120?**

*(1 hundred, 2 tens)*

■ **Any ideas on how we can take away 1?**

*(students respond by demonstrating and explaining their ideas)*

Then explain the difference between grouping in addition and in subtraction.

> **When we regroup in addition, we build groups or collections of 10 and move them to the next higher place. When we regroup in subtraction, we break up a group or collection of 10 and move what's left to the next lower place. Instead of building up we are breaking up the group. Let's see how it works.**

■ **Look at the first problem on Worksheet 3C. Can we take 1 from 0?**

*(no)*

■ **What do we have to do?**

*(borrow or regroup 1 ten)*

■ **If we break 1 ten into 10 ones and then take 1 of the ones away, how many ones do we have left?**

*(9)*

■ **How many tens do we have left?**

*(1)*

■ **How many hundreds do we have left?**

*(1)*

■ **What is another way to say 1 hundred?**

*(10 tens; 100 ones)*

■ **Look at the second problem. Can we take 1 away from 9?**

*(yes)*

■ **Builders, how will we subtract on our place value charts?**

*(take 1 away)*

Tell the builders and recorders to work together to complete the problems on the worksheet. Point out that they are to use the answers from each previous problem to make the next problem.

## Students discover patterns.

After students have completed *Worksheet 3C: Subtraction Recording Sheet,* discuss it with them.

■ **Did we have to regroup on the problem 110 – 1= ?**

*(yes)*

■ **When did we have to regroup again?**

*(100-5, 90-5, 80-5, 70-5, 60-5)*

■ **Can you see any pattern to this regrouping?**

*(have to regroup when a number is taken away from a ten)*

Then ask for two volunteers to demonstrate solving the problem 105 – 5 = ? Have one student build it on a place value chart in the front of the room and the other show it with digit cards on the digit chart.

■ **What is another way to say 105?**

*(1 hundred and 5 ones; 10 tens and 5 ones; 105 ones)*

■ **What is the answer to 105 – 5?**

*(100)*

■ **What is another way to say 100?**

*(10 tens; 100 ones)*

Now take 5 more away.

- **Who can tell me how to say this problem mathematically?**

  *(100 minus 5; 100 take away 5)*

- **What number do we have left?**

  *(95)*

- **If we take 5 more away how many do we have left?**

  *(90)*

- **Then subtract another 5?**

  *(85)*

- **Do you see a pattern? What is it?**

  *(counting down by five)*

# Part IV

# Addition and Subtraction on the Place Value Chart

## *Students add and subtract by building and recording algorithms.*

Organize students into pairs, one is a builder and one is a recorder. Distribute to each pair a desktop place value chart, 200 counting squares, paper clips, rubber bands, and *Worksheet 3D: Addition and Subtraction Recording Sheet.*

Explain to the students they are going to continue regrouping, but this time they will add and subtract. Instruct the builders to build the number 50 on the place value chart. Make sure all students have 5 tens in the tens place on their charts before continuing.

**Take away 3 from the 50. Build and record it.**

- **What is our answer?**

  *(47)*

**Now, add 7 to that answer. Build and record it.**

- **What is our answer?**

  *(54)*

Continue reading the numbers on Worksheet 3D for the students to add and subtract. After each problem ask for a volunteer to explain how their team solved it. To complete the worksheet, have students make up the rest of the problems, or you may prefer to create problems that you think your students need.

If students are more advanced, you might move into more sophisticated problems, such as the following:

■ What would have to be added to 111 to arrive at the answer 1,111?

■ What must be subtracted from 1,111 to leave 1,001?

■ If we had 1,000 boxes of cards and sold 909 of them, how many would we have left?

■ What number, when added to 110, equals 1,000?

# Part V

# Reinforcement Activities

## Activity 1: Shopping List Problems

Organize students into pairs or groups of three. Distribute to each group a desktop place value chart, 250 counting squares, paper clips, rubber bands, and *Worksheet 3E: Shopping List Problems*. To solve the shopping list problems, each group is to build their answers and record the algorithm (write the problem) on their worksheets.

Have students take turns building and recording. Discuss problems and answers with the group as a whole. You may wish to ask volunteers to demonstrate how they set up and solved the problems.

After the shopping list problems are solved, have each student group create a shopping problem for the other groups to build and record.

## Activity 2: Card Sharks

Organize students into pairs. Distribute to each pair a desktop place value chart, 250 counting squares, paper clips and rubber bands. Make sure each group has a pencil and paper.

Go around the room and ask each student to pick a card from a deck of playing cards. Ask each student, in turn, to say the number on their card. Numbered cards are worth face value, Jacks are worth 11; Queens are worth 12; Kings are worth 13; Aces are worth 1; and Jokers are worth 0.

As students say their numbers, direct the builder in each team to construct the number and either add it to (or subtract it from) the previous number on their place value chart. Direct the recorder to do the algorithm on a piece of paper.

## Activity 3: Digit Cards

Divide students into teams of three students. Distribute a copy of *Manipulatives 3A: Digit Cards*, and a pair of scissors to each student. Have students cut the worksheets into a set of digit cards. Turn the cards face down. Each student selects three cards.

**Round One: Make the Largest Number.** Each student uses 3 cards to make the largest possible number. The team with the largest number wins.

**Round Two: Make the Smallest Number.** Each students uses 3 cards to make the smallest possible number. The team with the smallest number wins.

**Round Three: One Thousand Total.** Each student uses 3 cards to make a number. The team that makes 3 numbers whose combined total is closest to 1,000 wins. Students should be allowed to trade digits among their team members and rearrange them before adding.

**Round Four: One Hundred Total.** Each student uses 3 cards to make a number. Teams have to subtract all 3 numbers from 1,000. The team whose answer is closest to 100 wins. Again, students should be allowed to trade digits among team members and rearrange them before subtracting.

Other activities students can do with the digit cards:

1. Order three-digit numbers from least to greatest.

2. Arrange digit cards so that when added, regrouping is required in the ones, tens, or hundreds place.

## Activity 4: Regrouping Practice

Have students use their desktop place value chart and 250 counting squares to regroup and add the following numbers:

9 tens + 16 ones

7 tens + 43 ones

12 tens + 19 ones

19 ones + 3 tens

1 hundred + 5 tens + 56 ones

# Part VI

# Assessment Opportunities

Each of the activities described in this unit, if modified slightly, can be used to assess student progress. Whenever you ask students to explain or demonstrate their understanding by using either concrete manipulatives or pictorial representations, you are informally assessing student knowledge and can use this assessment to guide future instruction.

Demonstrations and explanations are also powerful assessment tools. They can provide as much information about student understanding, and perhaps more, than written answers on a worksheet.

# UNIT FOUR

# UNDERSTANDING THE WRITTEN ALGORITHM

## Purpose of Unit

To help students understand that the written algorithm represents the regrouping process and provide practice adding and subtracting using manipulatives.

## Key Concepts

Traditional regrouping symbols (such as scratch marks and cross-outs) represent the grouping and trading of collections of ten.

## Blackline Masters

- Labels 4A: Whole Numbers for Human Place Value Chart
- Worksheet 4A: Hundreds Ledger (also make a transparency)
- Worksheet 4B: Thousands Ledger

## Other Materials

- Counting squares
- Desktop place value charts
- Dice (one for each pair)
- Overhead projector
- Paper clips
- Rubber bands

# Part I

# Subtraction with Ledgers and Place Value Charts

## *Review regrouping in addition and subtraction.*

Make one copy of *Labels 4A: Whole Numbers for Human Place Value Chart.* (Only the ones, tens, and hundreds labels are used in this unit.)

Ask for three volunteers to come to the front of the room and form a human place value chart. Give each student a label and have them stand in the correct place value order facing the class. Then, give 9 tens to the student who has the tens label. The other two students begin with nothing in their hands.

> **We've spent time adding, subtracting, and building numbers. Now, let's use this human place value chart to review the process of regrouping in addition and subtraction.**

- **What number does the human place value chart show?**

   *(90)*

- **What's another way to say that number?**

   *(9 tens and 0 ones; 90 ones)*

- **Who can show how to take 3 ones away from 90?**

   *(a student takes 1 ten from the person in the tens place, unclips it so there are 10 loose ones, takes 3 of the ones away, and hands 7 ones to the person in the ones place)*

- **How many tens are left?**

   *(8 tens)*

- **How many ones are left?**

   *(7 ones)*

- **What is the answer to 90 take away 3?**

   *(87)*

- **What is another way to say that number?**

   *(8 tens and 7 ones; 87 ones)*

When students have returned to their seats, instruct them to write the algorithm that was just demonstrated by the human place value chart. Then repeat the above process several more times with different algorithms.

## Relate regrouping to the method of cross-outs and number changes used in written algorithms.

Distribute desktop place value charts, 200 counting squares, paper clips, and rubber bands to each student.

Remind the students that many of them use scratch marks or cross-outs when they subtract. Demonstrate the process of subtracting 3 from 90 on the overhead using the traditional system of cross-outs and number changes.

> **We have 0 ones so we need to regroup or "borrow" 1 ten from the tens place, leaving us with 8 tens. Now we have 10 ones in the ones places. We take 3 away which leaves 7. Look at the tens place. We now have 8 tens. There are no tens to subtract, so we are left with 8 tens and 7 ones or 87.**

Have the students work out the same problem on their desktop place value charts. Then continue.

> **Now, let's try 87 – 8 = ? First, write the algorithm and work it out on your own. Then we'll have someone come up and do it on the overhead and explain the procedure. Finally, we'll prove the answer by doing it on our place value charts.**

When a student volunteer is demonstrating how to do the problem on the overhead, guide with the following questions:

- **Can we take 8 ones from 7 ones without regrouping?**

   *(no)*

- **Who can tell us what those scratch marks or cross-outs represent?**

   *(students explain in their own words that the cross-outs and scratch marks represent regrouping)*

- **How can we prove the answer using the place value chart?**

   *(student demonstrates with counting squares)*

Emphasize the importance of number position in the subtraction algorithm. Then explain that when adding it doesn't matter how you compute—top to bottom or bottom to top (commutative property)—but when subtracting the position of the two numbers is very important.

## Students subtract, using regrouping, and record the algorithm.

Organize students in pairs. Distribute a desktop place value chart, 200 counting squares, paper clips, and rubber bands to each pair. Hand out a copy of *Worksheet 4A: Hundreds Ledger* to each pair and put a transparency of it on the overhead.

Tell the students they are going to do more subtraction problems. Have students work with their partner: one person is a recorder and one person is a builder.

> **Builders, build 79. Recorders, write 79 on the first line of the ledger.**

Put the ledger transparency on the overhead and demonstrate where the recorders are to write the numbers.

Let's take 9 ones away from 79. Builders do it. Recorders, write 9 on the second line of the ledger and then subtract and write the answer on the third line.

**Worksheet 4A**

Name:_____

Date:_____

**Hundreds Ledger**

| Hundreds | Tens | Ones |
|---|---|---|
|  | 7 | 9 |
|  |  | 9 |
|  | 7 | 0 |
|  |  | 3 |
|  | 6 | 7 |
|  |  | 7 |
|  | 6 | 0 |
|  | 1 | 5 |
|  | 4 | 5 |
|  | 1 | 9 |
|  | 2 | 6 |

Name:_____

Date:_____

**Hundreds Ledger**

| Hundreds | Tens | Ones |
|---|---|---|
| 2 | 0 | 0 |
|  | 1 | 8 |
| 1 | 8 | 2 |
|  | 6 | 1 |
| 1 | 2 | 1 |
|  | 3 | 9 |
|  | 8 | 2 |
|  | 7 | 5 |
|  |  | 7 |
|  |  | 6 |
|  |  | 1 |

- **What do we have?**

  *(79 - 9 = 70)*

- **Did we have to regroup?**

  *(no)*

- **Why not?**

  *(there are enough ones in the ones place to subtract)*

Now, take 3 ones from 7 tens and 0 ones.

■ **What's the answer?**

*(67)*

■ **Did we have to regroup?**

*(yes)*

■ **Will someone come to the chalkboard to show us how you worked the problem?**

*(student goes to the board and writes the algorithm)*

■ **Builders, what did you need to do?**

*(take 1 ten from the tens place and break it into 10 ones; then take 3 away)*

**Next, let's take 7 ones away from the number 67.**

■ **What's the answer?**

*(60)*

■ **Did we need to regroup?**

*(no)*

■ **Why?**

*(there already were enough ones in the ones place)*

■ **Did we need to cross-out?**

*(no)*

■ **Why?**

*(there were enough ones and you didn't have to borrow)*

**Now, take 15 away from 60. Build and record.**

Encourage students to compare their answers with their partners. If pairs arrive at different answers using counting squares or ledgers, then they need to resolve these differences by reworking the problems together and discussing the process with one another. Also, have a volunteer demonstrate and explain the algorithm on the chalkboard. Make sure that students use the word *tens* when explaining subtraction in the tens column.

■ **What's the answer?**

*(45)*

**Let's complete our first ledger with one more problem. Subtract 19 from 45.**

Point out to students that another way to say that problem is 4 tens and 5 ones minus (or take away) 1 ten and 9 ones. Again, have a volunteer demonstrate and explain the answer.

■ **What's the answer?**

*(26)*

Let's switch roles. Those who were recorders are now builders and those who were builders are now recorders. Recorders, write 200 at the top of your second ledger. Work with your partner to subtract, one at a time, the following five numbers: 18, 61, 39, 75, 6.

When students are finished, compare and discuss the answers on their ledgers. Continue to reinforce the regrouping process of the place value chart and how it relates to the scratch marks or cross-outs we use when solving the algorithm.

## Students work with larger numbers and discover patterns.

When students are ready for more advanced problems, distribute a copy of *Worksheet 4B: Thousands Ledger* to each student. Students are not building on their place value charts, just solving the algorithm.

Write 1011 at the top of the first ledger on your worksheet. Subtract 99, each time, until you reach the bottom of the ledger.

Then have students circle each answer and look for patterns.

Write 1999 at the top of the other ledger. Subtract 89, each time, until you reach the bottom of the ledger.

Again, have students circle each answer and look for patterns.

# Part II

# Reinforcement Activities

## Activity 1: Three-digit computation with place value chart

Students should work in pairs for this activity. Using place value charts, 200 counting squares, pencils and paper, students do addition and subtraction problems. Assign one student the task of building the number on the place value chart while the other records and explains the answer.

| | | | |
|---|---|---|---|
| 120<br>−80 | 140<br>+60 | 100<br>−22 | 125<br>+47 |
| 101<br>+99 | 110<br>−99 | 100<br>−70 | 100<br>− 1 |
| 100<br>+ 9 | 100<br>− 9 | 100<br>−88 | 100<br>−10 |

## Activity 2: Target 1000

This game has two players who take turns rolling a single die. Each player will need a pencil and paper (Worksheet 4B could be used). Each player begins by writing the number 1000 on their paper. The object of the game is to stay as close to the number 1000 as possible after repeated additions or subtractions. To determine the number to add or subtract, players roll. The first roll tell hundreds; the second roll tells tens; and the last roll tells ones. The player chooses whether to add or subtract the number from 1000. The next player repeats the process. Players alternate turns, each time deciding whether to add or subtract from their last total. The player who is closest to 1000 after 10 turns is the winner!

There are several variations of this activity. You may wish to change the goal. For example, the student who has created the largest number (or the smallest) at the end of the round wins the game.

# Part III

# Assessment Opportunities

The subtraction problems in Activity 1 of the Reinforcement Activities could be made into a worksheet and used as a traditional assessment. To enhance this assessment, select 1 or 2 problems and then confer with students individually, asking them to explain the process.

Activity 2 in the Reinforcement Activities could be modified to assess addition and subtraction. Start with a different number this time. The goal, as before, is to stay as close as possible to that number. Instead of the students rolling dice, the teacher supplies the numbers.

Another good assessment opportunity is to ask the students to explain in writing the purpose of "scratch marks" in addition and subtraction. Don't expect the students to use your language to explain mathematical concepts. You are trying to determine whether they are able to express the concepts in their own words—an excellent indication of the student's personal understanding.

# UNIT FIVE

# REGROUPING WITH LARGE NUMBERS

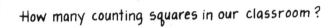

How many counting squares in our classroom?

|  | 100's | 10's | 1's |
|---|---|---|---|
| Group 1 | 500 | 40 | 2 |
| Group 2 | 400 | 10 | 8 |
| Group 3 | 300 | 30 | 1 |
| Group 4 | 700 | 20 | 6 |
| Group 5 | 300 | 10 | 4 |
| TOTAL | 2,200 | 110 | 21 |

## Purpose of Unit

To extend understanding of our place value system by counting, regrouping and renaming larger numbers. To introduce a nonproportional model (Decimal Dough) for regrouping and renaming.

## Key Concepts

Concepts of place value and regrouping provide the computational structure for addition and subtraction algorithms. Flexible regrouping is a characteristic of the base-ten system.

## Blackline Masters

- Assessment 5A: Flexible Regrouping

- Labels 4A: Whole Numbers for Human Place Value Chart

- Manipulatives 5A: Decimal Dough Bills

- Worksheet 5A: Tally Sheets

## Other Materials

- Colored transparency pens

- Counting squares

- Desktop place value charts

- Digit place value chart

- Overhead projector

- Paper clips

- Plastic bags

- Rubber bands

# Part I

# Flexible Regrouping

## Review place value concepts.

Organize students into small groups (four to six students). Distribute to each group a desk-top place value chart, paper clips, and rubber bands. Divide all the available counting squares among the groups. Be sure that more than 1,000 counting squares are distributed. Have plastic bags available to make thousandths.

> **Work with your group to build a number on your place value charts using all of your counting squares.**

## Introduce the thousands place.

Review with the students the activity they just completed.

> **We constructed a number, with all of our counting squares, using hundreds, tens, and ones.**

- **How many tens make 1 hundred?**

  *(10)*

- **What made up each ten?**

  *(10 ones)*

- **Can anyone guess what number we can build with 10 hundreds?**

  *(1 thousand)*

Then explain to the students that they are going to build a number in the thousands place. Take a plastic bag and walk around the room collecting enough hundreds from the students to make 1 thousand. Point out that they have been clipping tens, putting rubber bands around hundreds and now they will bag thousands.

> **Please count with me as I collect them—100, 200, 300 . . . 1000!**

- **How many hundreds are in a 1000?**

  *(10)*

- **Can you call 1000, 10 hundreds?**

  *(yes)*

- **If we wanted to build 1000 just out of tens, how many tens would we need?**

  *(100 tens)*

- **Let's prove that. How many tens make up 100?**

  *(10)*

- **How many tens are in 200?**

    *(20)*

Continue asking how many tens until you reach 1000.

## Discuss flexible regrouping of thousands.

Copy the table, below, on the overhead.

1000 = <u>1</u> thousand, 0 hundreds, 0 tens, 0 ones

1000 = <u>10</u> hundreds, 0 tens, 0 ones

1000 = <u>100</u> tens, 0 ones

1000 = <u>1000</u> ones

Use colored transparency pens. In the first row, underline the 1 group of thousand. In the second row, underline the 10 groups of hundreds. In the third row, underline the 100 groups of tens. In the bottom row, highlight 1000 ones.

Emphasize how the number 1000 can be viewed flexibly. In other words, the number of groups there are in 1000 differs depending on what's in each group.

Before continuing to the next segment, return to the students all the counting squares you collected to make a thousand.

## Students find the total of all the counting squares in the classroom.

Construct a table like the one in the illustration at the front of this unit, except without the numbers filled in. Have students help you fill in the amounts in each column. Then add columns to find the grand total of counting squares in the classroom.

> **Now, let's check our grand total by counting all the squares in the classroom.**

Follow the steps below, referring frequently to the significance of the collections of ten.

> **We'll combine all of our counting squares on one place value chart.**

- **Let's count ones and paper clip tens.**

    *(students help)*

- **Let's count tens and rubber band hundreds.**

    *(students help)*

- **Let's count hundreds and bag thousands.**

    *(students help)*

Have students help you add to find the total, which should be the same as the total on the table.

## Continue discussing flexible regrouping.

Use the grand total of the number of counting squares in your classroom to continue discussing flexible regrouping. For example, if the grand total was 2331, you would proceed as follows:

■ **How many thousands do we have in the number?**

*(2)*

■ **How many hundreds do we have in the number?**

*(3)*

■ **How many tens do we have in the number?**

*(3)*

■ **How many ones do we have in the number?**

*(1)*

■ **If we didn't group the hundreds into thousands, then how many hundreds would there be in this number altogether?**

*(23)*

Allow students to discuss this last question and come up with different ways for arriving at an answer. If students experience difficulty, then prove the answer by counting the groups of hundreds in the number or try the following line of questioning:

■ **How many thousands are in the number?**

*(2)*

■ **How many hundreds are in 1000?**

*(10)*

■ **If there are 10 hundreds in 1000, how many hundreds are there in 2000?**

*(20)*

■ **How many more hundreds are in the number, as well?**

*(3)*

■ **Then, how many hundreds are there in all?**

*(23)*

■ **Let's think of the number in another way. What if we regrouped the number 2331 into as many tens as possible, how many tens would that be?**

*(233)*

■ **How can we prove that answer?**

*(count the tens in each thousand, the tens in each hundred, and the tens in the tens place)*

Then continue to use the grand total of the number of counting squares in *your* classroom to make a table resembling the one below.

$\underline{2}331$ = 2 thousands, 3 hundreds, 3 tens, 1 one

$\underline{23}31$ = 23 hundreds, 3 tens, 1 one

$\underline{233}1$ = 233 tens, 1 one

$\underline{2331}$ = 2331 ones

You may want to repeat the same line of questioning for other numbers, in the thousands, to reinforce the concept of flexible regrouping.

> *It's very important to have students think aloud in order to describe the process they used to arrive at an answer. "Think alouds" allow you to assess understanding of the process, reinforce concepts, facilitate peer instruction and also give the students opportunities to develop language for expressing mathematical ideas.*

# Part II

# Regrouping Nonproportional Models: Decimal Dough

## Administer assessment.

Before introducing the play money, administer *Assessment 5A: Flexible Regrouping* to determine whether students are experiencing difficulty.

This short assessment will help determine whether students are ready to move on to more abstract representations of the regrouping and renaming process.

## Introduce Decimal Dough.

When students demonstrate comfort with the flexible regrouping process, introduce the system of money. Money is nonproportional because the bill representing $10 is not 10 times the size of the bill representing $1. It is also nonproportional because both a $1 bill and a $10 bill are each only one piece of paper.

> **Whenever we shop, we use a system that requires us to count, regroup, and rename numbers.**

■ **What is that system?**

*(the money system)*

- If the money system operated like the counting squares system, how much money would we have to lug around every day?

  *(students give various answers)*

  If we paper clipped one-dollar bills into tens, put rubber bands around hundreds or bagged thousands to buy houses or cars, we'd need to have a wheelbarrow for our money to pay in cash. However, in the money system we don't have to do that.

- Why not?

  *(because we have different bills for different dollar amounts)*

  That's right. With the money system we can trade in our 10 ones for a single ten-dollar bill. Or we can trade in 10 ten-dollar bills for 1 hundred-dollar bill and so on. This allows us to carry around a lot of money in a small wallet.

## Introduce the ten-thousands place and regrouping using Decimal Dough.

Use the blackline master *Manipulatives 5A: Decimal Dough Bills* to make enough Decimal Dough to distribute to each group 20 each of the following denominations: $10,000, $1000, $100, $10, and $1. Be sure students have their desktop place value charts. Organize students into groups of two or three.

Tell the students they are going to use a special money system called Decimal Dough to build larger numbers. Explain that in this system there are ones, tens, hundreds, thousands, ten thousands, hundred thousands, and millions.

- How does the Decimal Dough system differ from the real money system?

  *(in the real money system, we have 5-dollar bills, and 20-dollar bills)*

Designate one student in each group to be the "banker." Tell the students that instead of paper clipping, putting rubber bands around, or bagging as they did with counting squares, they may trade in smaller bills for larger denominations with the banker.

  Take out 11 thousands, 12 hundreds, 13 tens, and 11 ones. Think of a strategy for figuring out how much money that is.

Try some of the students' ideas. Then ask them to prove their answers by putting their Decimal Dough on their place value charts to figure out the total. Remind them to trade with the banker to regroup when possible.

- What did we do with our 11 ones?

  *(traded 10 ones for 1 ten-dollar bill and kept 1)*

- Then what did we do with our 14 ten-dollar bills?

  *(traded in 10 tens for 1 hundred-dollar bill and kept 4)*

- What did we do with our 13 hundred-dollar bills?

  *(traded in 10 hundreds for 1 thousand-dollar bill and kept 3)*

■ **What did we do with our 12 thousand-dollar bills?**

*(traded in 10 thousands for 1 ten thousand-dollar bill and kept 2)*

Point out to students that they've discovered they need a new place on their place value chart—theirs only goes up to the thousands place.

> **Oops! We need a new place on our charts for ten thousands. The name tells us exactly what the collection is called—10 groups of thousands or 1 ten thousand.**

After students have regrouped and traded they should have the number $12,341 constructed on their desktop place value chart with the 1 ten-thousand dollar bill lying on their table to the left of their thousands place.

Then using the overhead, demonstrate how the total can also be arrived at algorithmically. Write the dollar amounts that the students started with and have the students help you add to find the total. This lets students see how traditional addition mirrors the process they used to construct the total on their place value charts.

$$
\begin{array}{r}
\$11{,}000. \\
1{,}200. \\
130. \\
+\quad 11. \\
\hline
\$12{,}341. \\
\end{array}
$$

# Part III

# Flexible Regrouping with Five Digits

*Students build and regroup in the ten-thousands place using Decimal Dough.*

Organize students into pairs. Distribute to each pair a desktop chart and the following Decimal Dough: 10 millions, 10 hundred thousands, 20 ten thousands, 20 thousands, 20 hundreds, 20 tens, and 20 ones.

> **Take out 1 ten thousand-dollar bill, 8 thousand-dollar bills, 5 hundred-dollar bills, 7 ten-dollar bills, and 4 one-dollar bills. Use all of this money to build the total amount on your charts. Just pretend you have a ten-thousands place to the left of the thousands place on your charts.**

■ **How much money is this?**

*($18,574)*

Write 18,574 on the overhead or chalkboard and explain that the way a number is written and ordered tells how many thousands, hundreds, or tens are in the number.

> **This number has 1 ten thousand, 8 thousands, 5 hundreds, 7 tens, and 4 ones.**

Then underline the 1 in the number 18,574, on the overhead, to show 1 group of ten thousand.

- ■ **If we didn't use any ten-thousand dollar bills to build this number, but used thousand-dollar bills instead, how many would we need?**

  *(18 thousands)*

- ■ **How can we prove that answer?**

  *(student demonstrates how to trade in 1 ten thousand for 10 thousands and adds that number to the 8 already there)*

- ■ **Can everyone show it on your charts to prove it?**

  *(students do it)*

Return to the overhead and write the number 18,574 again. Underline the 18 to emphasize there are <u>18</u> thousands in the number.

**We can view this number as made up of 18 thousands, 5 hundreds, 7 tens, and 4 ones.**

- ■ **Suppose we traded in the thousand-dollar bills for hundred-dollar bills, then how many hundreds would we have?**

  *(185 hundreds)*

- ■ **How can we prove that?**

  *(each thousand is made up of 10 hundreds, so 18 thousands equals 180 hundreds and with the 5 hundreds we already have it totals 185 hundreds)*

Returning to the overhead, write the number 18574 again (without the comma). This time underlining the 185 to show that there are <u>185</u> hundred dollar bills in this number.

**We view this number also as 185 hundreds, 7 tens, and 4 ones.**

- ■ **If I wanted to know how many tens are in the number, how could I find that out?**

  *(student explains and demonstrates process)*

- ■ **How many tens are in the number?**

  *(1,857 tens)*

Write the number 18574 again, this time underlining the <u>1857</u> to show that there are 1857 tens in this number.

**We can also think of this number as 1,857 tens and 4 ones.**

- ■ **How many one-dollar bills are in this number?**

  *(18,574)*

Write the number 18574 again, underlining the entire number to show that there are <u>18574</u> one-dollar bills in the number. The list of numbers on the overhead should look like the following:

$$\underline{1}8574 = 1 \text{ ten thousand, 8 thousands, 5 hundreds, 7 tens, 4 ones}$$

$$\underline{18}574 = 18 \text{ thousands, 5 hundreds, 7 tens, 4 ones}$$

$$\underline{185}74 = 185 \text{ hundreds, 7 tens, 4 ones}$$

$$\underline{1857}4 = 1857 \text{ tens, 4 ones}$$

$$\underline{18574} = 18574 \text{ ones}$$

Review the same procedure using other numbers.

# Part IV

# Reinforcement Activities

## Activity 1: Counting and Regrouping with Decimal Dough

This activity emphasizes the regrouping concept. It has particular value because it narrows the focus of regrouping to only two places. Divide the class into three groups. Distribute the play money among the three groups in the following way:

**Group 1: all of the ten-dollar and hundred-dollar bills**

**Group 2: all of the thousand-dollar and ten-thousand-dollar bills**

**Group 3: all of the one-hundred-thousand- and million-dollar bills**

Ask the students to count and regroup the bills. Assist those who are experiencing difficulty.

## Activity 2: Regrouping with Decimal Dough and Recording on Tally Sheets

This activity expands place value to hundred thousands and millions. Organize students into pairs. Distribute to each pair a place value chart, random amounts of Decimal Dough, and a copy of *Worksheet 5A: Tally Sheet.* Ask the students to count and regroup their Decimal Dough to find a total. They should keep track of denomination subtotals on the tally sheet. Put a transparency of Worksheet 5A on the overhead and demonstrate how to use it.

After all groups have discovered their total "net worth" in Decimal Dough, walk around the room collecting, counting, and regrouping all of the ten thousands. Repeat with thousands, then hundreds, tens, and finally, ones. Once the Decimal Dough has been collected, total the separate quantities on the overhead and with the class, regroup where necessary.

## Activity 3: Shopping List with Decimal Dough

Students work in groups of two or three for this activity. Each group generates a shopping list of expensive items and their hypothetical costs, such as a house for $235,000, a yacht for $100,000. Record students' suggestions on the overhead.

Give each group approximately $500,000 of Decimal Dough. Each group chooses the items they wish to purchase, totals the cost and then shows the total amount on the place value chart using Decimal Dough. When groups have finished, add their totals together to determine how much the whole class spent.

---

> *Students may have trouble regrouping and trading with larger quantities. Difficulty with the algorithmic process signals a need for more work with manipulatives. Be sure to provide additional experiences counting, regrouping and renaming large numbers using concrete representations.*

---

## *Activity 4: Human Place Value Chart Using Decimal Dough*

Ask seven volunteers to serve as a Human Place Value Chart. Give each student one of the following labels: *ones, tens, hundreds, thousands, ten thousands, hundred thousands, and millions.*

Give the group 1 million dollar bill and tell them they must give 1 dollar to the teacher as a service fee. Have the group demonstrate the process of regrouping while you document the algorithm (1,000,000 − 1 = 999,999). Guide the students through the process by conducting think alouds and asking pertinent questions.

# Part V

# Assessment Opportunities

This unit contains both formal and informal evaluation opportunities. *Assessment 5A: Flexible Regrouping* is a formal method for assessing student understanding of the place value system and flexible grouping. However, each of the activities accompanying this unit could also be used for assessment of student knowledge and skill.

The whole number pretests from Unit One *(Assessment 1A: Whole Numbers* and *Assessment 1B: Whole Numbers Applications)* should be administered as post-assessments before moving on to the next unit. Comparing student performance before and after instruction provides an opportunity to measure student growth across all concepts. Moreover, it provides critical information about student readiness to learn decimal concepts.

Working with individuals and groups during small group activities also offers excellent opportunities for informal assessment.

# UNIT SIX

# DECIMAL FRACTIONS: TENTHS

## Purpose of the Unit

To introduce decimal concepts and notation, in particular, the concept of tenths, the symbol (decimal point), and the correct mathematical language to express decimal fractions.

## Key Concepts

The organizational structure of the place value system operates the same with decimal fractions as it does with whole numbers. The decimal point separates whole numbers and decimal fractions in a mixed number and precedes the decimal fractions.

## Blackline Masters

- Assessment 6A: Decimal Concepts
- Assessment 6B: Decimal Applications
- Assessment 6C: Tenths Review
- Transparency 6A: Counting Squares—Tenths (2 copies)
- Worksheet 6A: Decimal Word Problems
- Worksheet 6B: Composing Decimal Problems

## Other Materials

- Counting squares (tenths)
- Desktop place value charts
- Digit place value chart
- Overhead projector
- Scissors

# Part I

# Decimal Pretests

### *Administer assessments.*

Before initiating instruction, administer *Assessment 6A: Decimal Concepts* and *Assessment 6B: Decimal Applications* as pretests.

If your students have had prior instruction in fractions or decimals, these pretests will provide valuable information about the students' conceptions and help determine the level of instruction that best meets their needs. If this material is new, then pretesting will provide a baseline for assessing growth.

# Part II

# Introducing Tenths

### *Review and relate place value concepts to decimals.*

Review the place value system and explain to students that knowing whole number place value will help them understand decimals.

> **Many students have told me that they think decimals are hard. I think you'll find them easier to learn when we connect them to something we already know—the base-ten place value system.**

Write the number 3,092 on the chalkboard.

> **Let's review.**

> ■ **In the number 3,092, what does the 2 represent?**
>
> *(2 ones)*

> ■ **What does the 9 represent?**
>
> *(9 tens)*

> ■ **How about the 0, what does it represent?**
>
> *(0 hundreds)*

> ■ **And the 3?**
>
> *(3 thousands)*

> ■ **Look at the ones, again. What would happen if we added 8 more to the ones place?**
>
> *(we'd have 10 ones and would group them to make a ten)*

- **If we took this 1 ten and added it to the 9 tens, then what would we have?**

  *(10 tens, or 1 hundred)*

- **How would that number be written?**

  *(3,100)*

- **How would you say that number?**

  *(3 thousand, 1 hundred)*

- **Who can say that number another way?**

  *(31 hundreds; 310 tens; 3,100 ones)*

## Introduce tenths.

Throughout the rest of the book the students will be exploring decimals. For this reason, provide large counting squares made from *Manipulatives 1A: Large Counting Squares.*

For this unit, do not use all four different kinds of large counting squares. Use only those that are divided into tenths. Each student needs several tenths counting squares and a pair of scissors. Distribute the place value charts to students and have the digit place value chart in view. Put *Transparency 6A: Counting Squares—Tenths* on the overhead.

Remind students that they have been using their desktop place value charts folded over because they were working with whole numbers. Have them open up their charts and read the place names that are to the right of the decimal point.

Then direct attention to the transparency on the overhead.

> **We are going to continue to work with collections of ten, but this time with *a collection of ten that equals one.* Each of your counting squares is divided into ten equal sections.**

- **Does anyone know what we call each of these small pieces?**

  *(tenths)*

Draw a square on the chalkboard and divide it into ten unequal pieces.

- **Is each of these pieces 1 tenth?**

  *(students respond)*

> **I'm pleased you are willing to guess. We cannot call each of these pieces 1 tenth even though there are ten of them. To call each of these 1 tenth, the pieces must be of *equal* size.**

Compare the chalkboard drawing of unequal pieces to one of the counting squares on the transparency. Then hold up a paper counting square that is divided into tenths. While students watch, cut it into 10 equal parts.

- **What is one of these parts called?**

  *(1 tenth)*

Explain that there are several ways to write 1 tenth. Elicit from the students or tell them the following three ways: a decimal (.1); a fraction (1/10); in words (one tenth). Write each on the chalkboard.

■ **How can we show 2 tenths on a counting square on the overhead?**

*(student shades in 2 tenths on one square)*

■ **How can we show 2 tenths on our place value charts?**

*(cut up a tenths counting square and put 2 pieces in the tenths place)*

■ **Who will come up and show 2 tenths on our digit place value chart?**

*(student volunteers)*

■ **Who will shade in 3 tenths on the counting square on the overhead?**

*(student volunteers)*

■ **Would someone tell us how we can show 3 tenths on our place value charts?**

*(cut off another tenth and put it on our charts)*

■ **Who will show 3 tenths on our digit place value chart?**

*(student volunteers)*

■ **Who can write 3 tenths in another way?**

*(3/10; three tenths)*

Continue this activity with several other examples, such as 5 tenths or 7 tenths.

**Next, let's show 10 tenths.**

As students help you shade the counting square on the overhead, point out that 10 tenths equals 1 whole.

**That means 1 one and 0 tenths. Let's review, for a moment, how the place value system works.**

■ **What happens when we have a collection of 10?**

*(we regroup or trade)*

■ **So, what will we do with our 10 tenths?**

*(trade in our 10 tenths for 1 whole)*

**Everyone do it.**

■ **Who will come up to our digit chart and show it?**

*(student volunteers)*

Then write 10/10 = 1.0 on the chalkboard and explain that it can be written that way.

**The 10 tenths stand for 1 one and 0 tenths.**

*When teaching rational number concepts, two mathematical ideas,* partitioning *and* equivalence, *are of utmost importance.* Partitioning *is the notion of sharing equally—not just dividing, but dividing into equal portions.* Equivalence *is the concept of representing the same amount in different ways.*

## Administer informal assessment.

Before moving on to mixed numbers, administer *Assessment 6C: Tenths Review* as an informal assessment to make sure students are grasping the concept of tenths.

## Introduce mixed numbers.

Put a clean copy of *Transparency 6A: Counting Squares—Tenths* on the overhead.

- **How can we show 11 tenths using these counting squares?**

    *(student demonstrates)*

Be sure the student shades in 1 whole counting square and 1 tenth in another counting square on the transparency.

- **What else could we call 11 tenths?**

    *(1 one and 1 tenth)*

- **Who can write 1 and 1 tenth?**

    *(1.1)*

- **Is there any other way to write 1 and 1 tenth?**

    *( 1 1/10; 11/10)*

    **We have just written a mixed number.**

- **Why do you think it is called that?**

    *(because it's a whole number and part of a whole number)*

## Clarify the role of the decimal point.

Continue the discussion in the previous segment by pointing to the decimal point in the number 1.1 on the chalkboard.

> **Let's think about the decimal point and what it means. This symbol, the decimal point, is very important. It designates a part of a whole.**

Write 3.27, 32.7, 327. on the overhead.

> **Even though these digits are all the same, the placement of the decimal point changes the amount.**

- **Can anyone tell me how?**

  *(students guess)*

- **If these were amounts of money which would you want and why?**

  *(327 because that's the largest amount of money; 32.7 would be 32 dollars and change; 3.27 would be 3 dollars and change)*

  **We must learn to read numbers in mathematics the same as we learn to read words in reading.**

Explain that the first place to the right of the decimal point is called the tenths place. Put a decimal point on the chalkboard and write the word "tenths" after it (.tenths).

- **What is the place to the *left* of the decimal point called?**

  *(ones)*

Tell the students that the decimal point is read "and." Explain that the word "and" signifies a separation between wholes and parts.

  **When we read mixed numbers we must always say the word "and" for the decimal point.**

Write 15.7 on the overhead and read it out loud as you write out the words. Do the same with several other mixed numbers. Then write another number and ask the students to read it to their neighbor. Finally, have students practice writing and reading mixed numbers with a partner.

# Part III

# Reinforcement Activities

## Activity 1: Decimal Word Problems

Students work alone or in pairs for this activity. Distribute *Worksheet 6A: Decimal Word Problems*. Instruct students to read the problem, shade when necessary, and write the answer three ways—as a decimal, as a fraction, and in words.

## Activity 2: Composing Decimal Problems

Students work individually on this activity. Give each student a copy of *Worksheet 6B: Composing Decimal Problems*. Have students compose three story problems and shade in the sections of the counting squares to show their answers. If students need assistance, you may wish to spend some time composing story problems with them before distributing the worksheet.

  **Note: This story problem activity must be completed before moving on to the next unit.** The problems generated by the students on Worksheet 6B serve as the basis for the first activity in Unit Seven.

# Part IV

# Assessment Opportunities

This unit has three assessments, two are formal assessments and one is considered an informal assessment. Although the two formal assessments *(Assessment 6A: Decimal Concepts* and *Assessment 6B: Decimal Applications)* are designed to provide information on students' prior knowledge of decimals and mixed numbers, they can be used as post-assessments to measure growth in understanding.

Worksheet 6A and Worksheet 6B also provide informal assessment information on students' abilities to depict tenths and express them in written mathematical form.

In addition, assessment information is available throughout the lesson whenever students discuss, explain, or demonstrate their knowledge using concrete representations.

Assessments should reflect the multiple representations used to teach the mathematical concepts and processes to students. In other words, they should require students to demonstrate their understanding in a variety of ways.

# UNIT SEVEN

# DECIMAL FRACTIONS: HUNDREDTHS

| 1,000 thousands | 100 hundreds | 10 tens | 1 ones | .1 tenths | .01 hundredths | .001 thousandths |

## Purpose of the Unit

To introduce the concept of hundredths, examine the relationship of hundredths to tenths, and compare and order mixed numbers through the hundredths place.

## Key Concepts

In order to compare decimals they must be converted to the same unit or place value.

## Blackline Masters

- Assessment 7A: Tenths and Mixed Numbers

- Assessment 7B: Ordering Decimals

- Manipulatives 7A: High Decimal Rummy

- Transparency 7A: Counting Squares—Tenths and Hundredths (3 copies)

- Transparency 7B: Tenths Overlay

- Worksheet 7A: Sixteen Counting Squares

- Worksheet 7B: Shading and Naming Equivalences

## Other Materials

- Colored transparency pens

- Completed Worksheet 6B: Composing Decimal Problems

- Counting squares (tenths, hundredths)

- Desktop place value charts

- Overhead projector

- Scissors

# Part I

# Correct Match: Tenths

## Students play a game with problems generated in unit six.

*Worksheet 6B: Composing Decimal Problems* must be completed to begin this unit. Cut the completed worksheets in half so that the three story problems are separated from the three shaded counting squares. Give each student one of the halves with three shaded counting squares and keep all the story problems. Organize the class into small groups of three to four students.

> **Today we're going to play a game called Correct Match. I will read the problems you wrote. Confer with your team, then raise your hand if you have the answer. The first group to match all its counting squares is the winner.**

Explain to students their answers will only be correct if they use the proper mathematical language to express them. This is a good time to reinforce correct language usage, such as seven tenths, instead of point seven.

## Administer assessment.

Once the students finish playing the Correct Match game, administer *Assessment 7A: Tenths and Mixed Numbers*.

Make sure that students write their answers in three different ways, on the assessment sheet. That will help you determine whether students are ready to move on to hundredths.

# Part II

# Introducing Hundredths

## Determine students' prior knowledge of hundredths.

Tell the students that before they move on to hundredths you want to find out what they already know.

> **Let's take a few minutes to brainstorm what we know about hundredths. We can also think of questions we'd like answered. I'll record your comments and then later we will come back to what I've written to make sure your questions are answered.**

Make a table on chart paper or a transparency with the headings "What I Know" and "Questions I Have." If students find it difficult to discuss hundredths, help them with guiding questions:

■ Why would hundredths be the next place value we're going to study?

- Are hundredths larger or smaller than tenths?

- Why is this place called hundredths?

These student responses will be used at the end of this unit for an informal assessment.

## Introduce hundredths and regrouping decimal fractions.

Organize students into pairs. Identify one partner as "A" and the other as "B." Distribute to pairs a desktop place value chart, scissors, 2 tenths counting squares, and 2 hundredths counting squares.

**Let's look at the transparency. The first square is divided into 10 equal parts.**

- **What is each part called?**

   *(tenths)*

   **Use 1 of your counting squares that is divided into 10 parts. A's, cut and build 1 tenth on your place value chart. B's, check A's work and tell whether you agree or disagree and why.**

Make sure that all groups have 1 tenth in the tenths place.

**Look at the other kind of counting square.**

- **Instead of 10 equal parts, how many equal parts does this counting square have?**

   *(100)*

- **What might each of these equal parts be called?**

   *(hundredths)*

Have students clear their place value charts. Then explain how you want them to build 1 hundredth.

   **Use one of your counting squares that's divided into 100 parts. B's, cut it into 10 tenths. Next cut one of those tenths into 10 hundredths. Put 1 hundredth in the hundredths place on your chart.**

- **What do we have on our place value chart now?**

   *(1 hundredth)*

- **B's, add another hundredth to the chart. A's, what do we have now?**

   *(2 hundredths)*

- **B's, add another hundredth to the chart. A's, what do we have now?**

   *(3 hundredths)*

- **B's, add another hundredth to the chart. A's, what do we have now?**

   *(4 hundredths)*

- **A's, add 4 more hundredths. B's, how many do we have now?**

  *(8 hundredths)*

- **A's, add 2 more hundredths. B's, what do we have now?**

  *(10 hundredths)*

Remind students that when they worked with whole numbers, 10 ones became 1 ten, 10 tens became 1 hundred, 10 hundreds became 1 thousand, and so on.

- **Who remembers what happens when we have a collection of 10 tenths?**

  *(10 tenths became 1 whole)*

- **Now we have 10 hundredths. So what do you think that will become?**

  *(1 tenth)*

Have the class count their 10 hundredths together and out loud. Then instruct the A's to regroup on their place value charts.

- **Can someone explain the regrouping process to the class?**

  *(trade in 10 hundredths for 1 tenth and put the 1 tenth in the tenths place)*

- **Is 10 hundredths equivalent to, or the same amount as, 1 tenth?**

  *(yes)*

## Students build and write hundredths.

Continue from the previous segment with students assigned as A's or B's. Put *Transparency 7A: Counting Squares—Tenths and Hundredths* on the overhead. Have available *Transparency 7B: Tenths Overlay* and *Worksheet 7A: Sixteen Counting Squares*.

Shade in .03 on one of the hundredths counting squares. Draw a circle around the 97 hundredths that are not shaded.

- **Who can tell me what portion of the whole is shaded?**

  *(3 hundredths)*

- **Who can tell me what portion is not shaded?**

  *(97 hundredths)*

- **How can we prove that the amount circled is 97 hundredths? Who can explain?**

  *(the whole is divided into 100 equal parts so if 3 parts are shaded then 97 parts are left unshaded)*

  **Let's build 97 hundredths on our desktop charts. Don't forget to regroup if needed.**

Be sure students are showing 97 hundredths with 9 tenths and 7 hundredths on their charts.

- **Who can read the amount on your chart in two different ways?**

  *(9 tenths and 7 hundredths; 97 hundredths)*

Next, let students watch as you shade in 20 hundredths on a hundredths counting square on the transparency.

■ **I have shaded 20 of the 100 parts. Who can read this number for me?**

*(20 hundredths)*

**B's, build 20 hundredths on your place value chart. A's, check your teammate's work.**

If the students place all 20 hundredths in the hundredths place, stop and discuss the need to regroup. Emphasize that 20 hundredths is regrouped into 2 tenths even though the number can be read as 20 hundredths or 2 tenths.

■ **Who can write this decimal?**

*(volunteer writes .20)*

■ **Is there another way to write that number?**

*(20/100)*

Tell the students there is another way to show how tenths and hundredths compare. Show them *Transparency 7B: Tenths Overlay* and point out the counting squares on it are divided into tenths.

**Watch very closely as I overlay a counting square that is divided into tenths on top of the counting square that has 20 hundredths shaded.**

■ **How many tenths are shaded?**

*(2)*

■ **How can we express the amount shaded as tenths?**

*(.2)*

■ **How can we express the amount shaded as hundredths?**

*(.20)*

■ **Which is more, 2 tenths or 20 hundredths?**

*(they are equivalent, or the same amount)*

■ **Who can write .20 = .2 on the board?**

*(volunteer does it)*

Next, shade in 8 tenths on a tenths counting square on the transparency.

■ **How many tenths are shaded?**

*(8)*

■ **Who can write that amount?**

*(student writes .8)*

■ **What is another way I can write that amount?**

*(8/10, eight tenths)*

- How many hundredths would I have to shade in to get the same amount?

   *(80)*

- Who can write the decimal fraction and read it?

   *(.80; eighty hundredths)*

Provide several more examples, relating tenths and hundredths. Also point out that 10 tenths or 100 hundredths are equivalent to one whole.

   To provide additional practice relating tenths and hundredths give students copies of *Worksheet 7A: Sixteen Counting Squares.* Have students shade in the amounts as you say or write some of the following pairs of numbers: 1 tenth/10 hundredths; 10 tenths/100 hundredths; 5 tenths/50 hundredths; 6 tenths/60 hundredths.

# Part III

# Comparing Decimal Quantities

## *Relate decimals to fractions.*

Put a clean copy of *Transparency 7A: Counting Squares—Tenths and Hundredths* on the overhead and shade 6 tenths.

- Who can tell me what decimal fraction is shaded?

   *(6 tenths)*

- Who can write this as a decimal and as a fraction?

   *(volunteer writes .6, 6/10)*

- Can anyone write this amount in hundredths?

   *(60 hundredths; .06; 6/100)*

- How many tenths are not shaded?

   *(4)*

- Who can write the unshaded amount as a decimal and as a fraction?

   *(.4; 4/10)*

- How do you express the unshaded amount in hundredths?

   *(40 hundredths; .04; 4/100)*

- How many tenths make 1 whole counting square?

   *(10)*

- How many hundredths make 1 whole counting square?

   *(100)*

Emphasize that 10 tenths make 1 whole and 100 hundredths also make 1 whole. Therefore, 10 tenths *equals* 100 hundredths.

■ **Who can write this mathematically in different ways?**

*(10/10 = 100/100; 10 tenths equals 100 hundredths; 1.0 = 10/10; 1.00 = 100/100)*

■ **How can there be 100 hundredths in 1 whole and also only 10 tenths in 1 whole?**

*(we can divide a whole into 10 equal parts or 100 equal parts)*

## *Introduce principles for comparing non-equivalent decimals.*

Continue from the previous segment with 6 tenths still shaded on the transparency. Distribute desktop place value charts, several tenths counting squares, several hundredths counting squares, and scissors to each student. Have students sort their counting squares into a pile of tenths and a pile of hundredths. Have available another clean copy of *Transparency 7A: Counting Squares—Tenths and Hundredths.* Let students watch while you shade 1 more tenth, so 7 tenths are shaded.

■ **How many hundredths should we shade to show an amount equal to 7 tenths?**

*(70)*

■ **May I have a volunteer shade that amount?**

*(student shades 70 hundredths)*

Then write .73 and .8 on the chalkboard and ask students to predict which one is larger. Do not give the correct answer at this time, but ask students to explain their thinking.

> **Let's prove the answer. Use your pencils to shade 8 tenths on one of your whole tenths counting squares and 73 hundredths on one of your whole hundredths counting squares.**

Discuss the results and point out to students they showed that 8 tenths is larger than 73 hundredths, even if 73 hundredths sounds larger than 8 tenths.

> **In whole numbers, the more digits in the number, the larger the number. For example, 73 is larger than 8. In decimals, however, more digits doesn't always mean a larger number.**

Tell students that shading is only one way we can prove 8 tenths is larger than 73 hundredths.

> **Another way we can prove which is larger is to convert the numbers to the same place value or fractional unit.**

■ **What can we convert 8 tenths to so we can compare it to 73 hundredths?**

*(hundredths)*

■ **8 tenths equals how many hundredths?**

*(80)*

■ **Which is larger, 80 hundredths or 73 hundredths?**

*(80 hundredths)*

*It is extremely important to emphasize the distinction between decimal fractions and whole numbers. This may be a source of confusion for students. Many students assume that decimal fractions parallel whole numbers and that the largest decimal fraction is the one with the most digits.*

Put a clean copy of *Transparency 7A: Counting Squares—Tenths and Hundredths* on the overhead. Write 1.05 on the chalkboard or overhead.

■ **Who can read that number for me?**

*(student reads 1 and 5 hundredths)*

■ **Who can shade that amount on the overhead—using the hundredths counting squares?**

*(student shades 1.05)*

While the volunteer is shading 1.05 on the overhead, have students shade the same amount using their own hundredths counting squares. Next write 1.5 on the chalkboard.

■ **Who can read that number for me?**

*(student reads 1 and 5 tenths)*

■ **Who can shade that amount on the overhead—using the tenths counting squares?**

*(student shades 1.5)*

Again, while the volunteer is shading 1.5 on the overhead, have students shade the same amount using their own tenths counting squares.

■ **Which number, 1.05 or 1.5, covers the greater amount?**

*(1.5)*

■ **Which number has the most digits in it?**

*(1.05)*

■ **Which number is larger?**

*(1.5)*

■ **How do you know?**

*(1 and 5 tenths is equivalent to 1 and 50 hundredths which is more than 1 and 5 hundredths)*

Next instruct the students to shade 2.03 using hundredths counting squares and to shade 2.3 using tenths counting squares.

■ **Who can write both numbers?**

*(students respond)*

■ **Which number is larger?**

*(2.3)*

- **How do you know?**

  *(2 and 3 tenths is equivalent to 2 and 30 hundredths which is more than 2 and 3 hundredths)*

## Compare mixed numbers.

Write the numbers 35.5 and 35.05 on the chalkboard. Ask the students which number is larger. Have students explain their answers.

> Many of you have some good ideas. I'm going to show you the process I use. First I look at the largest place.

- **What is the largest place in these two numbers?**

  *(the tens place)*

- **How many tens do we have in each number?**

  *(3 tens)*

  > Since they are the same we can't tell which number is larger (or smaller) just by looking at the tens.

- **Where should we look next?**

  *(the ones place)*

  > Exactly, we look at the next largest place which, in this case, is the ones place.

- **What do we find?**

  *(both numbers have 5 ones)*

  > Correct. We can't determine which number is largest by looking at the tens or ones because they both have the same number of tens and ones. We need to look at the decimal places.

- **Where should we look first?**

  *(the tenths place)*

- **What do we find in the tenths place?**

  *(one number has 5 tenths and the other has 0 tenths)*

- **So what does that tell us?**

  *(35.5 is larger than 35.05)*

Continue leading students through the process using different decimal fractions and mixed numbers, such as the following pairs: 13.31 to 13.13; 32.01 to 32.1; 34.55 to 35.45.

# Part IV

# Ordering Decimals

## *Students order mixed numbers.*

Write the following mixed numbers on the overhead or chalkboard: 213.5; 203.4; 230.7; 203.04; 203.43. Explain to the students they are going to order the numbers from largest to smallest using the same procedure they used in comparing pairs of decimals.

- **In this list of numbers, what place is largest?**

  *(hundreds)*

- **Can you tell which number is largest by looking at the hundreds place only?**

  *(no, they all have 2 hundreds)*

- **What should you compare next?**

  *(tens place)*

- **Can you tell which number is largest now?**

  *(yes)*

- **Which is largest?**

  *(230.7)*

Point out the number with 2 hundreds and 3 tens is the largest because it has more tens than the other numbers. Start a list with the number 230.7 at the top.

- **Which number would be next largest?**

  *(213.5)*

- **How do we know?**

  *(the other numbers have 0 tens and this number has 1 ten)*

Write it in the second position on the list.

- **Where do we look now to compare the remaining 3 numbers?**

  *(the ones place)*

- **Can we tell which is the third largest number by looking at the ones place?**

  *(no, because all the numbers that are left have the same number in the ones place)*

- **Then where will we look?**

  *(the tenths place)*

  There are three numbers left. Two of these numbers have 4 tenths and one number has 0 tenths. We might not know which number is the next largest, but we should know which is the smallest.

**Who knows which number is smallest?**

*(203.04)*

- **How do we know that?**

*(the other two numbers have 4 tenths and that number doesn't have any tenths)*

Write 203.04 at the bottom of the new list leaving space above it.

- **How do we decide which of the two remaining numbers with 4 tenths is larger?**

*(look at the hundredths place)*

- **How many hundredths are in the number 203.4?**

*(0 hundredths)*

- **How can we show that there are no hundredths in this number?**

*(write a 0 in the hundredths place)*

Remind students that 4 tenths is equivalent to 40 hundredths. Explain that now it's easy to compare 203.40 and 203.43 because they are converted to the same place value.

- **Where would these fit in our list?**

*(203.43 comes first and is followed by 203.4)*

Write both numbers in the appropriate positions to complete the list.

Next use the procedure above to have students order the following list of numbers, but this time from smallest to largest: .37; .7; .73; .43; .8.

If students are having difficulty ordering the numbers, have them build the numbers on their place value charts to make comparisons. For example, divide students into five groups (if there are five numbers) and have each group build one of the numbers. Have the class order the numbers by looking at the place value charts.

---

*Don't be discouraged if students need several lessons working with decimal fractions and mixed numbers involving tenths and hundredths. With experience, students will develop a more enriched mathematical schema and you will be able to pick up the pace of instruction.*

---

## Administer assessment.

Administer *Assessment 7B: Ordering Decimals.* Have students work independently to order the two series of numbers.

If students need more practice, do a similar activity to the one described in the previous segment: building numbers on place value charts in order to make comparisons. However, this time divide the students into groups of three, four, or five and give each student in the group a different mixed number to build. Then ask students to work with their group members to order the numbers they constructed on the place value chart, from largest to smallest or vice versa. This activity is most valuable when the numbers look similar. Try the following numbers: 32.4, 34.2, 43.01, 32.44, and 32.04.

*Students summarize what they have learned about decimals.*

Make sure each student has a pencil and paper. Ask students to list and summarize what they have learned over the past several days. In their own words, students might come up with some of the following:

- Hundredths means that the whole is divided into 100 equal parts.

- Tenths means that the whole is divided into 10 equal parts.

- 1 tenth is 10 times larger than 1 hundredth or 1 hundredth is 1/10 the size of 1 tenth.

- It takes 10 hundredths to equal 1 tenth and 10 tenths to equal 1 whole.

- By comparing the values of each place, we can order decimals and mixed numbers from largest to smallest and vice versa.

Record whatever the students come up with on the chalkboard. Compare this new list with the statements and questions that students generated during the brainstorming session in Part II.

> Remember earlier we made of list of things we knew and questions we had about hundredths.

- Would we change anything on our original list?

- Would we add anything to our original list?

- Have any of our questions on our original list been answered?

- Do we have any new questions to add to our list?

Before continuing with the next unit and introducing thousandths, make sure students understand the difference between tenths and hundredths and can compare and order decimal fractions and mixed numbers. The up-coming mathematical content increases both in quantity and complexity, so if you move too quickly the students will become confused and retain far less of what is taught.

# Part V

# Reinforcement Activities

## *Activity 1: High Decimal Rummy*

Organize students into groups of three. Distribute a copy of *Manipulatives 7A: High Decimal Rummy* to each group. Have students cut the worksheet into individual cards. A dealer in each group shuffles the cards and deals 1 card to each player, including herself. Dealer puts the rest of the cards face down on the table with 1 card facing up.

Each player, in turn, decides whether to exchange their card for the face-up card or draw a new card and exchange it for the card in their hand, depending on which card shows the higher number.

When each player has had one turn, the round is over. At this point, all players compare the card they're holding. The player with the highest number keeps all three cards. The game continues for three rounds. The player who has accumulated the most cards wins.

## Activity 2: Shading and Naming Equivalences

Distribute *Worksheet 7B: Shading and Naming Equivalences* to each student. Have students shade in the counting squares to represent equivalent quantities and write the corresponding decimal numeral. Once they've completed the worksheet, students should compare and discuss their answers with a partner.

# Part VI

# Assessment Opportunities

There are two formal assessments in this unit *(Assessment 7A: Tenths and Mixed Numbers* and *Assessment 7B: Ordering Decimals).*

Throughout this unit there are many opportunities for informal assessment. For example, when students explain their answers or prove them using pictures or manipulatives, they indicate whether or not they understand the material. Additionally, having students summarize in their own words what they have learned provides an excellent opportunity for informal assessment.

# UNIT EIGHT

# APPLICATIONS: TENTHS AND HUNDREDTHS

## Purpose of Unit

To review the relationship between tenths and hundredths. To provide real world problem-solving experiences computing mixed numbers.

## Key Concepts

Place value in decimals, like the denominators in fractions, communicates the number of equal parts into which a whole is divided. Decimals follow the same regrouping and trading rules as whole numbers.

## Blackline Masters

- Assessment 8A: Tenths and Hundredths Review

- Assessment 8B: Decimal Fractions

- Transparency 8A: Counting Squares—Hundredths

- Transparency 7A: Counting Squares—Tenths and Hundredths (6 copies)

- Worksheet 8A: Subtraction Story Problems

- Worksheet 8B: Ordering and Computing Prices and Weights

- Worksheet 8C: Comparing and Computing Distances

## Other Materials

- Counting squares (tens, ones, tenths, hundredths)

- Colored transparency marking pens

- Desktop place value charts

- Envelopes (two for each pair)

- Overhead projector

- Rubber bands

- Scissors

## Part I

# Review Decimal Concepts

### *Administer assessment.*

Administer *Assessment 8A: Tenths and Hundredths Review.*

When students have completed the assessment put *Transparency 8A: Counting Squares—Hundredths* on the overhead. Ask volunteers to explain their answers on the assessment by shading the counting squares on the transparency. While the class is reviewing the answers, quickly scan their assessment sheets to determine which students are still experiencing difficulty. Set aside some time to work with students who are still struggling with tenths and hundredths.

### *Review ordering of tenths and hundredths and finding equivalences.*

Put a copy of *Transparency 7A: Counting Squares—Tenths and Hundredths* on the overhead and have available several more clean copies. To review, point to one of the tenths counting squares on the transparency.

■ **What would we shade on this counting square to show 20 hundredths?**

*(2 tenths)*

Point to one of the hundredths counting squares.

■ **What would we shade on this counting square to show 2 tenths?**

*(20 hundredths)*

■ **What's another way to write that?**

*(.20, 20/100, twenty hundredths, 1/5)*

Next explain to the students that they are going to compare the size of some decimals. Write .6 and .58 on the chalkboard or overhead.

■ **Who can shade .6?**

*(student does it)*

■ **Who can shade .58?**

*(student does it)*

■ **Which is the larger quantity?**

*(6 tenths)*

■ **Who can shade and write 75 hundredths?**

*(student does it)*

■ **Who can shade and write 7 tenths?**

*(student does it)*

Point to one of the partially shaded counting squares.

- ■ **If we wanted to show 1 whole, how much more would we need?**

  *(students respond)*

- ■ **How did you arrive at that answer?**

  *(answers vary)*

Point to any two of the counting squares.

- ■ **If we wanted these counting squares to each show the same amount, what would we have to do?**

  *(students respond)*

- ■ **What is another way we could do it?**

  *(answers vary)*

- ■ **If we wanted to find out how much more .6 is than .58 what could we do?**

  *(answers vary)*

- ■ **If we wanted to find out how much more .75 is than .7 what could we do?**

  *(answers vary)*

# Part II

# Regrouping Decimals on the Place Value Chart

## *Students build and record to review addition process.*

Distribute to each pair a desktop place value chart, 1 tenth counting square, 1 hundredth counting square, scissors, and paper. Identify a builder and a recorder in each pair. Have three different colored marking pens and put a clean copy of *Transparency 7A: Counting Squares—Tenths and Hundredths* on the overhead.

> **Builders, cut up your hundredths counting square and put 2 hundredths on your chart. Recorders, write that amount on your paper.**

Check to be sure that builders and recorders have done it correctly.

> **Add 3 hundredths. Builders, build it. Recorders, record the problem and solve it.**

Make sure that the recorders have a problem that looks like this:

$$
\begin{array}{r}
.02 \\
+.03 \\
\hline
.05
\end{array}
$$

Now, add 5 more hundredths. Builders, build it. Recorders, write a new problem and solve it.

■ **What is our answer?**

*(10 hundredths or 1 tenth)*

■ **What should we do when we have a collection of 10 hundredths?**

*(group them together and trade for 1 tenth)*

■ **How do we show this number on our place value chart?**

*(group 10 hundredths and trade for 1 tenth)*

■ **Who can write the problem on the chalkboard and explain it?**

*(student writes and explains)*

■ **What is another way to write 1 tenth?**

*(.1, .10, 1/10)*

Direct students' attention to the overhead and explain that you are going to show the problem they just solved in another way. Shade 2 hundredths with color A.

> **First, we built 2 hundredths on the place value chart, so I'll shade that amount.**

Shade 3 more hundredths with color B.

> **Next, we added 3 hundredths, so I'll shade that much more. Together that makes 5 hundredths.**

Shade in 5 more hundredths with color C.

> **Finally, we added 5 more hundredths. This gave us 10 hundredths or 1 tenth.**

Repeat the procedure above having students build, record and then shade to review the addition process. Provide them with sets of decimals that add up to 1 tenth so they have to regroup.

## Students build and record to subtract mixed numbers.

Make sure each pair has a desktop place value chart, 3 hundredths counting squares, and at least 12 tenths counting squares, scissors, and paper. Then give each pair two envelopes. Instruct the students to mark one envelope "tenths" and the other envelope "hundredths." Have the students cut up a tenths square and a hundredths square and save the pieces in the appropriate envelopes. Organize pairs into builders and recorders.

> **Builders, build 9 and 5 tenths on your place value chart. Recorders, write the number.**

■ **If we take away 3 and 4 tenths and what do we have?**

*(6 and 1 tenth)*

- **Who could explain the procedure?**

  *(take 4 tenths from 5 tenths leaving 1 tenth; take 3 ones from 9 ones leaving 6 ones)*

- **Who can write the problem?**

  *(volunteer writes:)*

$$\begin{array}{r} 9.5 \\ -3.4 \\ \hline 6.1 \end{array}$$

Explain to students that now you want them to take 5 more tenths away.

- **Who can write the problem?**

  *(volunteer writes:)*

$$\begin{array}{r} 6.1 \\ -.5 \\ \hline \end{array}$$

- **Can we take 5 tenths from 1 tenth?**

  *(no)*

- **What do we need to do?**

  *(take 1 from the ones place, cut it up into 10 tenths and put them into the tenths place)*

- **How many tenths should we have in our tenths place now?**

  *(11)*

- **If we take 5 tenths away, how many will we have left?**

  *(6 tenths)*

Have the builders build the problem and the recorders write and solve it.

- **What is the answer?**

  *(5 and 6 tenths)*

- **Who can write and solve the problem?**

  *(student writes:)*

$$\begin{array}{r} 6.1 \\ -.5 \\ \hline 5.6 \end{array}$$

Continue the process above by subtracting each of the following numbers from the previous answer: 1.3, 2.9, .5, .17, .05. Be sure students change roles frequently so that each has ample opportunity to experience building and recording.

# Part III

# Solving Story Problems

## Discuss practical uses of decimals.

Ask students if they can give an example of where they see or use decimals. They may come up with some of the following:

- Radio station channels are expressed in mixed decimals. (92.1 FM)

- Gas is often measured in mixed decimals to the hundredths place. (12.75 gallons of gas)

- Body temperature is measured in mixed decimals. (98.6 degrees)

- Money is expressed in mixed decimal form. ($9.35)

## Students use manipulatives to show changes in body temperature.

Distribute to pairs a desktop place value chart, tens and ones counting squares, an envelope of at least 20 tenths, one rubber band, and paper. Identify a builder and recorder in each pair.

Point out to the students that mixed numbers are commonly used to measure and record body temperatures.

- **What is a normal body temperature?**

  *(98.6 degrees or 98 and 6 tenths)*

- **If you have a fever, is your body temperature higher or lower than 98.6?**

  *(higher)*

Write the following numbers on the chalkboard: 100.2; 99.8; 98.3; 98.6; 101.8.

- **Which of these numbers represent a fever?**

  *(100.2; 99.8; 101.8)*

Tell builders and recorders to work together to build the number 98 and 6 tenths—a normal body temperature—on their place value charts.

> **The number we have constructed represents Judy's normal temperature. Last week she got the flu and her temperature shot up 5 tenths of a degree.**

Have students work with their partners to show Judy's new temperature on the place value chart.

- **What do we need to do?**

  *(add 5 tenths to the tenths place)*

- **How many tenths do we have now?**

  *(11)*

- **What do we need to do?**

  *(trade 10 of the tenths for 1 whole)*

- **What is Judy's temperature now?**

  *(99.1 degrees)*

- **Who can write and solve the problem to show the increase in Judy's temperature?**

  *(volunteer writes:)*

  98.6
  + .5
  ―――
  99.1

- **Why are the numbers in this problem lined up this way?**

  *(numbers are lined up according to their place value so that you will add tenths to tenths, ones to ones, and tens to tens)*

- **How did we build 99 and 1 tenth?**

  *(student shows 9 tens, 9 ones and 1 tenth)*

**So we all agree that Judy's temperature rose to 99.1 degrees. But, before long her temperature went up 1 and 6 tenths degrees more. Builders, build her new temperature. Recorders, solve the problem on paper.**

While students work, check to see if the builders trade 10 ones for 1 ten and then 10 tens for 1 hundred and if the recorders set up the problem correctly.

- **Who can write and solve the problem on the chalkboard?**

  *(student writes:)*

  99.1
  + 1.6
  ―――
  100.7

If the student sets it up correctly, reiterate that tenths were added to tenths, ones to ones, and tens to tens. If the student sets up the problem incorrectly, guide them through the process while you write and solve the algorithm on the chalkboard.

- **What is Judy's new temperature?**

  *(100.7 degrees)*

- **How did we show her temperature on our place value charts?**

  *(1 group of 100 in the hundreds place and 7 tenths in the tenths place)*

Point to the 0 in the tens place.

- **What does this 0 tell us?**

  *(there are no tens in the tens place)*

Point to the 0 in the ones place.

- **What does this 0 tell us?**

  *(there are no ones in the ones place)*

Just before bedtime, Judy's temperature rose another 1 and 7 tenths degrees. Builders and recorders figure out her new temperature.

- **What is Judy's new temperature?**

  *(102.4)*

The next morning Judy's mother was relieved to see that it had dropped 1 and 5 tenths of a degree. Builders and recorders figure it out.

- **Does she still have a fever?**

  *(yes)*

Let's review how we worked it out.

- **Who can write and solve the problem on the chalkboard?**

  *(student writes:)*

  102.4
  - 1.5

- **Why are the numbers lined up this way?**

  *(so tenths are underneath tenths and ones are underneath ones)*

- **What happened when we tried to take 5 tenths away from the tenths place?**

  *(couldn't take 5 tenths away because there were only 4 tenths in the tenths place)*

- **What did we have to do then?**

  *(trade in 1 whole for 10 tenths, put them in the tenths place which makes 14 tenths, then take 5 tenths away which leaves 9 tenths)*

- **How can we show that step on the problem on the chalkboard?**

  *(cross out the 2 ones and show that 1 one is left, then cross out the 4 and write 14 above it to show that we now have 14 tenths, then subtract)*

- **What is Judy's temperature now?**

  *(100.9)*

Then continue with more problems of Judy's fever.

- **By late afternoon, Judy's temperature dropped another 8 tenths of a degree. What is her temperature now?**

  *(100.1)*

- **The next morning Judy's mother knew that she was definitely on the road to recovery. Her temperature had returned to 98.6 degrees. How much did it drop overnight?**

  *(1.5)*

*Regrouping and trading decimal fractions and mixed numbers follow the same sequence as that of whole number addition and subtraction. However, because decimals are a less familiar concept, concrete practice and guided instruction setting up and solving problems simultaneously with numbers and manipulatives allows students to see the relationship between concrete and abstract representations.*

## Review the decimal point.

Make sure each student has pencil and paper. Explain to the students that they're now going to use what they've learned about tenths to solve mixed-number problems involving hundredths. Have available *Worksheet 8A: Subtraction Story Problems.*

> **Yesterday I went shopping and bought two kinds of bulk food. I bought 1.3 pounds of crackers and 1.28 pounds of pretzels.**

Write the amounts on the chalkboard.

- **First, which weighs more?**

  *(crackers)*

- **If we wanted to find out how much more the crackers weighed, then what would we have to do?**

  *(subtract)*

Ask a student to write the problem on the chalkboard. Do not give the student any directions about where to place the decimal points or which number belongs on top and which on the bottom. If the student lines up the decimal points correctly, ask the class why the student organized the problem that way.

If the decimal points are placed incorrectly, or the problem is organized incorrectly, ask the students to try working the problem that way. Discuss the process and their results. Review the importance of lining up the decimal points when subtracting.

> **As in whole number addition and subtraction, decimal numbers have to be lined up according to their place value. Tenths should be lined up with tenths, hundredths with hundredths. That means the decimal points will be lined up as well.**

Through the process of exploration, discussion, and discovery, the problem should end up written on the chalkboard as follows:

$$\begin{array}{r} 1.3 \\ -1.28 \\ \hline \end{array}$$

- **Is it possible to take 8 hundredths away from 0 hundredths?**

  *(no)*

- **How can this problem be solved?**

  *(put a 0 in the hundredths place in the number 1.3)*

- **Why can we do this?**

  *(because 3 tenths is equivalent to 30 hundredths)*

- **What's left when 1 and 28 hundredths is taken away from 1 and 30 hundredths?**

  *(2 hundredths)*

- **Two hundredths of what?**

  *(2 hundredths of a pound)*

- **Suppose we wanted to find out how many pounds of snack food we had altogether? What would we need to do?**

  *(add the numbers 1.28 and 1.3)*

Have a student solve the problem on the chalkboard. Then ask students to make up a number problem and write it so the decimal points are lined up correctly and then write it so the decimal points are lined up incorrectly. Have students explain which is correct and why.

Give students *Worksheet 8A: Subtraction Story Problems.* Ask them to solve the problems arithmetically and to also shade the quantities on the counting squares.

## Administer assessment.

Before starting the next unit administer *Assessment 8B: Decimal Fractions.* Have students complete the items independently. Their performance on this worksheet will determine whether added review is needed before moving on to Unit Nine and introducing thousandths.

# Part IV

# Reinforcement Activities

### Activity 1: Ordering and Computing Prices and Weights

Students may work individually or in partners for this activity. Give each student a copy of *Worksheet 8B: Ordering and Computing Prices and Weights.* The students order the prices and the weight of the candy and solve problems.

### Activity 2: Comparing and Computing Distances

Give each student a copy of *Worksheet 8C: Comparing and Computing Distances.* Students may work individually or in pairs to solve the problems. If they encounter difficulty, use counting squares to build the numbers or to shade in the amounts.

# Part V

# Assessment Opportunities

This unit begins and ends with a formal assessment. *Assessment 8A: Tenths and Hundredths Review,* administered in the beginning of this unit, can help you determine how well students are grasping the concept of tenths and hundredths. *Assessment 8B: Decimal Fractions,* administered at the end of the unit, provides information about the student's ability to compare and solve problems involving tenths and hundredths.

Worksheets 8B and 8C could also be used as assessments if students completed them independently. Reviewing the worksheets as a group provides additional opportunities for reteaching or clarifying concepts.

# DECIMAL FRACTIONS: THOUSANDTHS

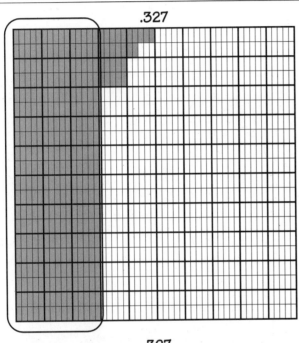

.327

.3 = .30 = .300

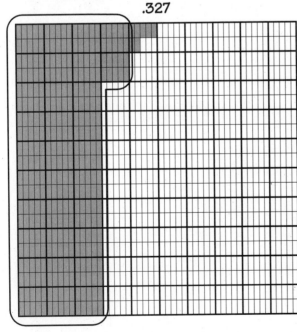

.327

.32 = .320

.327 = .3 + .02 + .007
or
.327 = .32 + .007
or
.327 = .327

## Purpose of the Unit

To introduce the concept of thousandths and examine its relationship to tenths and hundredths.

## Key Concepts

The relative size and value of thousandths can be predicted by extending the concepts of the base ten system. Understanding place value is crucial to comparing and ordering decimals.

## Blackline Masters

- Assessment 9A: Tenths, Hundredths, Thousandths Review

- Manipulatives 9A: Place Value Cards

- Manipulatives 1A: Large Counting Squares (Make 2 transparencies.)

- Transparency 9A: Large Counting Square—Thousandths

- Worksheet 9A: Counting Squares—Thousandths (3 copies per student; also make a transparency)

- Worksheet 9B: Counting Squares—Tenths, Hundredths,Thousandths (3 copies per student; also make a transparency)

## Other Materials

- Colored pencils

- Colored transparency pens

- Counting squares (tenths, hundredths, thousandths)

- Desktop place value charts

- Overhead projector

- Scissors

# Part I

# Introducing Thousandths

## *Discuss patterns of grouping and trading.*

Review the key patterns of regrouping and trading in the place value system.

> You've worked with the place value system from millions to hundredths. There is a pattern in the number system that holds true for decimals as well as whole numbers.

> ■ **What is the pattern?**
>
> *(whenever you have a collection of 10 you have to regroup)*

Have students help construct the table, below, on the chalkboard or overhead. Save room at the top of the table for more information that is added later.

> Let's start with the smallest decimal we have studied—hundredths. When we have a collection of 10 hundredths we regroup them into 1 tenth. As we complete this table, let's look for patterns.

| | | |
|---|---|---|
| 10 hundredths | = 1 tenth | = .1 |
| 10 tenths | = 1 one | = 1.0 |
| 10 ones | = 1 ten | = 10.0 |
| 10 tens | = 1 hundred | = 100.0 |
| 10 hundreds | = 1 thousand | = 1,000.0 |
| 10 thousands | = 1 ten thousand | = 10,000.0 |
| 10 ten thousands | = 1 hundred thousand | = 100,000.0 |
| 10 hundred thousands | = 1 million | = 1,000,000.0 |

If students still need to experience the regrouping process concretely, have them use counting squares and their place value charts to demonstrate each row of the table until they run out of squares.

> Our table shows what happens in our base-ten system when we have a collection of ten in any place. Sometimes, however, we need to break up, or bust up, a collection of ten.

> ■ **Can anyone tell us when we have to break up, or bust up, a group of ten?**
>
> *(sometimes when we subtract)*

Have students help construct another table which allows them to see the pattern in reverse.

This time lets start with 1 million. If we had to break 1 million up, in order to subtract, we could make it 10 hundred thousands. As we complete this table, let's look for patterns.

| | | |
|---|---|---|
| 1 million | = 1,000,000.0 | = 10 hundred thousands |
| 1 hundred thousand | = 100,000.0 | = 10 ten thousands |
| 1 ten thousand | = 10,000.0 | = 10 thousands |
| 1 thousand | = 1,000.0 | = 10 hundreds |
| 1 hundred | = 100.0 | = 10 tens |
| 1 ten | = 10.0 | = 10 ones |
| 1 one | = 1.0 | = 10 tenths |
| 1 tenth | = .1 | = 10 hundredths |

Keep both tables available for discussion in the next segment.

## Introduce thousandths.

Make two transparencies of *Manipulatives 1A: Large Counting Squares* and cut the squares apart. Cut one of the hundredths counting squares into 10 equal pieces. From one of the thousandths counting squares cut out 10 tiny thousandths pieces. (A handy way to handle these tiny pieces is to spread them out on the table, only slightly, and put a piece of clear tape on top of them to hold them in place. When you lift up the tape the pieces will come up.) Keep scissors available.

Put the whole hundredths counting square on the overhead.

■ **How many tenths would we have if we divided this counting square into tenths?**

*(ten)*

**Yes, 10 tenths equals 1 whole. Here, I have already cut one up.**

Put all 10 pieces of the hundredths counting square that you have already cut up on the overhead. Point to 1 of the pieces.

**Now I want to cut up one of these tenths pieces into hundredths. Watch me while I cut one of them up.**

While students are watching, cut one of the tenths pieces into 10 hundredths pieces.

■ **How many hundredths do we have?**

*(10 hundredths)*

**Now let's suppose we took 1 of these hundredth pieces and divided it into 10 equal pieces. Here, I have already cut one up.**

Put the 10 tiny thousandths pieces that you already cut up on the overhead.

- **What would each of these teeny little parts be called?**

  *(thousandths)*

- **Can anyone guess why we would call one of these tiny parts a thousandth?**

  *(because there are 1000 parts in 1 whole)*

Hold up a whole thousandths counting square.

- **How do we know that this counting square is divided into 1000 parts or thousandths?**

  *(each of the hundredths are divided into 10 parts and 10 groups of 100 equal 1000)*

Return to the two tables that the students helped create in the last segment. Direct students' attention to the table that goes from small to large.

**Let's add to the top of the this table: 10 thousandths = 1 hundredth = .01.**

Then direct students' attention to the table that goes from large to small.

**Let's add to the bottom of this table: 1 hundredth = .01 = 10 thousandths.**

Next encourage students to look at the table to identify patterns. Write 1.0 and 1 on the chalkboard and point out that's how 1 is written. Write .1 on the chalkboard and point out that's how 1 tenth is written. Write .01 on the chalkboard and point out that's how 1 hundredth is written.

- **How can 1 thousandth be written?**

  *(.001)*

- **If we were to add these four numbers together, (1, .1, .01, .001) what would our total be?**

  *(1.111)*

- **How can we say that number?**

  *(1 and 1 hundred 11 thousandths)*

Go over the problem, stressing the place value of the 1 in each number and the importance of aligning the place values and the decimal point correctly.

# Part II

# Creating Thousandths

## *Students shade counting squares to create thousandths.*

Put a transparency of *Worksheet 9A: Counting Squares—Thousandths* on the overhead and distribute a paper copy of it to each student.

Write the number 1.111 on the chalkboard and ask students to shade in the amount on their worksheets. Give students a few minutes to complete the task. Then collect the worksheets and use them as a reference for guiding your discussion.

Review with the students how to shade the number 1 and 111 thousandths. Emphasize that 111 thousandths can be thought of as 1 tenth plus 1 hundredth plus 1 thousandth.

> To show the amount 1.111, a whole counting square needs to be shaded in first.

- **Who will shade in 1 whole on the overhead?**

  *(volunteer shades)*

> Then 111 thousandths need to be shaded on another counting square. One way is to count and shade 111 of these tiny little squares. But that would take a long time. Another way is to use our knowledge of decimals.

Point to the tenths place in the number 1.111.

- **What place is this?**

  *(tenths)*

- **How many tenths are there in this decimal fraction?**

  *(1)*

- **Who can shade 1 tenth on the overhead?**

  *(volunteer shades 1 tenth)*

- **How many hundredths are in this number?**

  *(1)*

- **Who can shade an additional 1 hundredth?**

  *(volunteer shades 1 hundredth)*

Point out to the students that so far they have shaded 1 whole plus 1 tenth plus 1 hundredth.

- **Who can read that number for me?**

  *(1 and 11 hundredths)*

- **How many thousandths are in this number?**

  *(1)*

- **Who can shade an additional 1 thousandth?**

  *(volunteer shades 1 thousandth)*

- **1 thousandth is so tiny, who can see it from where you are sitting?**

  *(students respond)*

## *Demonstrate flexible regrouping with decimal fractions.*

Distribute another copy of *Worksheet 9A: Counting Squares—Thousandths* to students. Put *Transparency 9A: Large Counting Square—Thousandths* on the overhead. Shade 327 thousandths on it and ask students to do the same on their worksheets.

Tell students they can confer with their neighbors. After students have finished the task, direct their attention to the transparency on the overhead showing the correct shading of 327 thousandths.

■ **If we wanted to take the time to count every tiny little square or thousandth, how many squares would be colored in?**

*(327)*

**That's right. Let's count to make sure I colored in the correct number.**

■ **How many thousandths are in each hundredth?**

*(10)*

**Let's count 10 thousandths, 20 thousandths, 30 thousandths, 40 thousandths, . . ., 320 thousandths, 321 thousandths, 322 thousandths, . . ., 327 thousandths.**

Tell the students you want them to look at the number .327 in different ways. With a colored transparency pen draw a ring around the 3 shaded tenths.

■ **How many tenths are in our number 327 thousandths?**

*(3)*

Point out that in the number .327, 3 tenths can also be seen as 30 hundredths or 300 thousandths. If you sense that students do not see these equivalencies, then count to prove that .3 = .30 = .300.

**Look at the shaded portion that does not have a ring around it.**

■ **How many hundredths are in this part of the number?**

*(2)*

■ **Who can tell me how many hundredths that is in all?**

*(32)*

■ **Who can help me count all the hundredths to prove?**

*(students respond)*

Then draw a ring around all the hundredths with a different colored transparency pen.

**Think carefully about this next question.**

■ **Thirty-two hundredths is equivalent to how many thousandths?**

*(320)*

■ **How many more thousandths are in .327?**

*(7)*

Write the following on the chalkboard as you summarize: .327 = .3 + .02 + .007 or .32 + .007 or .327.

Help students repeat the steps described above using the numbers .222; .987; .013 on the remaining counting squares of their worksheet.

# Part III

# Comparing and Ordering Decimal Quantities

## Review place value of decimal fractions.

Distribute another copy of Worksheet 9A to each student. Ask the students which is greater, 1 tenth, 1 hundredth, or 1 thousandth. Continue after a discussion that generates the correct answer.

> In the first counting square, shade 7 tenths. In the second counting square, shade 7 hundredths. In the third counting square, shade 7 thousandths. In the fourth counting square, shade the total of these three numbers.

- ■ **Which is more: 7 tenths or 7 hundredths?**

  *(7 tenths)*

- ■ **What number did we get when we combined 7 tenths, 7 hundredths, and 7 thousandths?**

  *(777 thousandths)*

If students have difficulty combining decimal quantities, provide additional practice before moving on to the next activity.

## Students compare and order decimal fractions.

Distribute copies of *Worksheet 9B: Counting Squares—Tenths, Hundredths, Thousandths* to each student. Have available enough copies of the worksheet to give each student a second copy. Put a transparency of it on the overhead.

> Shade in 7 tenths on the first counting square and write the decimal on the line below. Shade in 51 hundredths on the second counting square and write the decimal. Shade in 457 thousandths on the third counting square and write the decimal.

Then have volunteers shade in the same quantities on the overhead while the class is watching. Give students a chance to correct errors on their own worksheets before continuing.

- ■ **Which number is the largest?**

  *(7 tenths)*

- ■ **How do we know?**

  *(a greater amount is shaded in)*

- ■ **Of the remaining two quantities, which is more?**

  *(51 hundredths)*

- ■ **So which is the smallest quantity?**

  *(457 thousandths)*

- **Who can write the numbers from largest to smallest, on the chalkboard?**

  *(volunteer writes .7; .51; .457)*

- **Who can read these decimals out loud?**

  *(volunteer reads them)*

- **Why does .457 look larger than .7 or .50?**

  *(it has more digits than the others)*

- **If these were whole numbers, not decimals, which one would be largest?**

  *(457)*

Then point out to students that it takes 100 thousandths to equal just 1 tenth. So 7 tenths is equivalent to 700 thousandths. Remind them that before they try to compare (or to add and subtract) decimals they should first convert them to the same place value or fractional unit.

- **If we convert them all to thousandths decimals, what would they be?**

  *(.700; .510; .457)*

Repeat the above procedure to compare more sets of numbers. Use the rest of the worksheet to compare these sets: .3; .33; .033 and .2; .45; .575.

Hand out a second copy of Worksheet 9B to compare these sets: .6; .65; .067 and .4; .37; .233 and .7; .08; .745. As students work, remind them of the importance of place value in comparing and ordering decimals.

Even though students understand tenths and hundredths, do not assume that they will be able to apply their knowledge to thousandths immediately. They still need ample opportunities to shade, compare, read, write, and order thousandths.

If students experience a lot of difficulty you may wish to review Unit Seven, this time expanding the activities to include thousandths.

# Part IV

# Comparing Decimal Quantities by Place

### *Review comparing decimal quantities.*

Give each student another copy of *Worksheet 9B: Counting Squares—Tenths, Hundredths, Thousandths.* Put a transparency of the same worksheet on the overhead. Also make sure each student has a colored pencil and a regular pencil.

> **Use your regular pencils to shade .2 in first square; .35 in the second square; and .125 in the third square. Also write the numbers.**

When the class has completed the task, shade and write the same amounts on the overhead while students watch.

Use your colored pencil and draw a ring around the tenths that are shaded on each of the three squares.

After the students finish, do the same on the transparency.

- **What did we draw a ring around in the first counting square?**

   *(2 tenths)*

- **What did we draw a ring around in the second counting square?**

   *(3 tenths)*

- **What did we draw a ring around in the third counting square?**

   *(1 tenth)*

- **Which number is the largest?**

   *(35 hundredths)*

- **How do we know?**

   *(.35 has more tenths than .2 or .125)*

- **Who can tell the numbers from largest to smallest?**

   *(.35; .2; .125)*

   **In the second row on your worksheets shade .8 in the first square; .83 in the second square; and .835 in the third square. Also write the numbers.**

When they finish, instruct students to use their colored pencils to draw a ring around the tenths that are shaded in each number.

- **Can we tell which of these three numbers is largest just by looking at the tenths place?**

   *(no)*

- **Why not?**

   *(because all three have the same number of tenths)*

   **Use your colored pencil and draw a ring around the hundredths in each number.**

- **Can we tell which number is largest by looking at the tenths and hundredths place?**

   *(no)*

- **Why not?**

   *(because 83 hundredths and 835 thousandths both contain 83 hundredths or 8 tenths and 3 hundredths)*

- **Which number is the smallest and how can we tell?**

   *(we know that 8 tenths is the smallest, because it doesn't have any hundredths or thousandths)*

- **Does that help us identify which is the largest?**

   *(no, we still don't know which number is the largest)*

Remind students that to compare decimals, we must first convert them to the same unit or place value.

   **Let's convert all of them to thousandths.**

- **.8 is equal to how many thousandths?**

   *(800 thousandths)*

- **.83 is equal to how many thousandths?**

   *(830 thousandths)*

- **What about .835?**

   *(it is already 835 thousandths)*

- **Which number is the largest?**

   *(.835)*

Some students may already know that 83 hundredths is larger than 8 tenths. They would not have to change each number into the same unit of measure. However, many students need this approach initially to direct their attention to systematic measures of comparison.

## *Administer assessment.*

Administer *Assessment 9A: Tenths, Hundredths, Thousandths Review.*

   Have students work independently to complete this cumulative assessment. After evaluating student performance, review and discuss responses to each item with the whole class. This will provide an opportunity to reteach troublesome concepts or clarify misconceptions.

# Part V

# Reinforcement Activities

## *Activity 1: Place Value Cards*

In this activity, students construct a place value chart from memory. Make enough copies of *Manipulatives 9A: Place Value Cards* to distribute a single set including the decimal point card to each student. Note that one copy of the blackline master has two sets of place value cards on it. Have students cut the eleven cards apart and arrange them in the correct place value order. Remind students to place the decimal point where it belongs.

   Another option is for students to work in groups to order the cards. Have students take turns selecting a card and placing it in the appropriate spot next to or between other cards.

## Activity 2: Shading & Ordering Decimal Quantities

Organize students into groups of three for this activity. Assign each student in the group the number 1, 2, or 3. Distribute counting squares to each group—6 whole tenths squares, 6 whole hundredths squares, 6 whole thousandths squares.

Write the number .8 on the overhead or chalkboard. Tell the "1's" to shade in that amount on a tenths counting square; the "2's" to shade in that amount on a hundredths counting square; and the "3's" to shade in that amount on the thousandths counting square. When all have finished the task, ask the group to compare quantities and discuss equivalence. Repeat the process with the following decimal fractions: .500; 1.0; .40; .2; .75. Then ask the groups to work together to order all of the numbers from largest to smallest.

# Part VI

# Assessment Opportunities

Throughout Unit Nine there are many opportunities to turn a segment of instruction into an assessment. For example, in Part III, if students work independently to shade in .7, .07 and .007 on Worksheet 9A, it could be used as an informal assessment. Or, when students are asked to compare and order sets of decimals on copies of Worksheet 9B, you might expand the activity to have students order all the numbers that you give them.

Finally, Unit Nine contains a formal cumulative assessment, *Assessment 9A: Tenths, Hundredths, Thousandths Review.* Reviewing, modeling and discussing student responses to each item provides important insights into students' understanding of decimal concepts and offers additional opportunities to reteach concepts or clarify misconceptions.

# UNIT TEN

# APPLICATIONS: THOUSANDTHS TO THOUSANDS

## Purpose of the Unit

To provide experience with a nonproportional model (Decimal Dough) for regrouping decimal fractions and mixed numbers to the thousandths, and solve simple addition and subtraction story problems involving thousandths.

## Key Concepts

Decimals follow the same regrouping rules as whole numbers.

## Blackline Masters

- Manipulatives 10A: Decimal Dough Coins

- Manipulatives 5A: Decimal Dough Bills

- Transparency 10A: Decimal Patterns Ledger (2 copies)

- Transparency 10B: Decimal Dough Coins for Overhead

- Transparency 9A: Large Counting Square—Thousandths (2 copies; also use as manipulatives)

- Worksheet 10A: Adding Thousandths (also make a transparency)

- Worksheet 10B: Subtracting Thousandths (also make a transparency)

- Worksheet 10C: Sports Problems (also make a transparency of the first page)

- Worksheet 10D: Counting Squares for Mixed Numbers (also make a transparency)

- Worksheet 10E: Robo-Batter

- Worksheet 10F: Decimal Dough Story Problems

- Worksheet 10G: Checkbook Problems

- Worksheet 10H: Kingdom of Wize Problems

- Worksheet 9A: Counting Squares—Thousandths (also make a transparency)

## Other Materials

- Counting squares (tenths, hundredths, thousandths)

- Crayons

- Desktop place value charts

- Scissors

## Part I

# Regrouping Thousandths on the Place Value Chart

### *Review equivalency.*

Put a copy of *Transparency 9A: Large Counting Square—Thousandths* on the overhead. Distribute to each student scissors, 5 tenths, 5 hundredths, and 5 thousandths whole counting squares.

> **Let's begin by reviewing equivalences. Use 1 of each of your tenths, hundredths, and thousandths counting squares. Cut 6 tenths from each of these three counting squares.**

> ■ **How do we know where to cut?**

> *(students respond in different ways)*

Direct attention to the overhead.

> ■ **Who can shade the equivalent of 6 tenths?**

> *(volunteer shades the equivalence of 6 tenths)*

> ■ **How many hundredths equal 6 tenths?**

> *(60)*

Write .6 = .60 on the chalkboard. Then have students help you prove by counting 10 hundredths, 20 hundredths, 30 hundredths, . . ., 60 hundredths.

> ■ **How many thousandths does it take to equal 6 tenths?**

> *(600)*

Write .6 = .60 = .600 on the chalkboard. Again, have students help you prove by counting 100 thousandths, 200 thousandths, 300 thousandths, . . ., 600 thousandths.

Have students repeat the process above of cutting a number from each of their tenths, hundredths, and thousandths counting squares and comparing them. Use the following numbers: .3; .400; .50. Then have students do the same for the number .79 which requires that they estimate on the tenths counting square.

### *Students build decimal fractions to the thousandths.*

Cut a copy of Transparency 9A into tenths. Then distribute to each student scissors, desktop place value charts, and a paper copy of Transparency 9A which they will use as a manipulative.

> **Note to Teacher:** Even if your class is using the Large Counting Squares, the thousandths pieces are rather small. So in this unit we suggest you use paper copies of *Transparency 9A: Large Counting Square—Thousandths* as the manipulative.

Explain to students that in a few minutes they are going to build .450 on their charts and then add .005 to that number. Write both numbers on the chalkboard.

**But first, let's review by showing it on the overhead.**

Put 1 tenth from the cut-up thousandths transparency on the overhead and guide students through a "think aloud."

■ **How many thousandths would that be?**

*(100 thousandths)*

Show 2 tenths.

■ **Then how many thousandths are in 2 tenths?**

*(200 thousandths)*

Show 3 tenths.

■ **How many thousandths are in 3 tenths?**

*(300 thousandths)*

Show 4 tenths.

■ **How many thousandths are in 4 tenths?**

*(400 thousandths)*

Point to .450 on the chalkboard.

■ **Now that we have 400 thousandths, how many more do we need to make .450?**

*(50 thousandths)*

Have students watch as you cut another tenths piece into 10 pieces.

■ **Does anybody know how much each of these pieces is?**

*(10 thousandths)*

■ **How many hundredths is that?**

*(1 hundredth)*

■ **Again, how many more thousandths do we need?**

*(50)*

**Let's count these pieces together: 10 thousandths, 20 thousandths, . . ., 50 thousandths. That makes 450 thousandths.**

Then remind students that they are going to add .005 to that number.

**Remember, each of these hundredths contains 10 thousandths.**

■ **Do we need the entire hundredth to add .005?**

*(no)*

■ **What shall we do?**

*(cut the hundredth up)*

- **How many thousandths do we want to add?**

  *(5)*

- **So, how many thousandths does that make altogether?**

  *(455 thousandths)*

Finally, have students cut up their thousandths square and build .450 on their charts and then add .005 to that number. Talk the students through the process.

## Students add and regroup decimal fractions.

Continue from the segment above. Students should have .455 built on their desktop charts. Organize pairs as builders and recorders. Distribute copies of *Worksheet 10A: Adding Thousandths* and put a transparency of it on the overhead.

> **Recorders, solve the algorithm in box 1 on your worksheet.**

- **What is the answer?**

  *(.455)*

- **Is that the same as the quantity on our chart?**

  *(yes)*

  > **Now, we are going to add another 5 thousandths to our answer. Builders, put 5 more thousandths on your charts.**

- **How many thousandths are in the thousandths place now?**

  *(10 thousandths)*

- **What happens when we have a collection of 10 in our number system?**

  *(we group them and trade them in for the next place)*

- **When we trade in our 10 thousandths what do we get in return?**

  *(1 hundredth)*

- **Who can tell me where to put the hundredth on the place value chart?**

  *(in the hundredths place)*

- **What is the new total?**

  *(460 thousandths, or 46 hundredths)*

  > **Recorders, notice that the algorithm in box 2 on your worksheet is the problem we just built on our charts. Solve it.**

Then direct attention to the overhead that has a transparency of Worksheet 10A on it.

- **Can someone tell me the answer to the problem in the first box and explain how you know?**

  *(.455; students respond)*

  > **Now, let's go over the second problem.**

- **When we add 5 thousandths to 5 thousandths, what do we get?**

  *(10 thousandths)*

- **What do we have to do?**

  *(trade the 10 thousandths for 1 hundredth)*

- **Do we have any thousandths now?**

  *(no)*

- **What do we do with this hundredth?**

  *(add it to the other hundredths)*

- **How many hundredths do we have now?**

  *(6 hundredths)*

- **What should be added next?**

  *(tenths)*

- **When we add 0 tenths to 4 tenths how much is that?**

  *(4 tenths)*

- **How many hundredths is 4 tenths?**

  *(40 hundredths)*

- **How many hundredths do we have in the number altogether?**

  *(46 hundredths)*

Point to the *0* in the thousandths place in the answer .460 and emphasize that it means there are *no* thousandths in the number.

- **Do we have any thousandths in the thousandths place on our place value charts?**

  *(no)*

Point to the 6 in the hundredths place in the answer .460 and emphasize that it means there are 6 hundredths in the number.

- **Do we have 6 hundredths in the hundredths place on our place value charts?**

  *(yes)*

Point to the 4 in the tenths place in the answer .460 and emphasize that it means there are 4 tenths in the number.

- **Do we have 4 tenths in the tenths place on our place value charts?**

  *(yes)*

Instruct students to continue adding 5 thousandths to build new numbers until they reach 550 thousandths, completing the worksheet.

> **Builders, build. Recorders, write and solve each algorithm on your worksheet. Each time be sure to discuss and compare the quantity on your charts with the answers on your worksheets.**

As students work, emphasize the relationship between regrouping the manipulatives and the system of "cross-outs and changing numbers" in addition.

## Students discover patterns and make predictions.

Continue from the previous segment. Put *Transparency 10A: Decimal Patterns Ledger* on the overhead and tell students you are going to record their answers from *Worksheet 10A: Adding Thousands.* Record the answers as students read outloud.

**Look at the numbers we have recorded on this ledger.**

■ **What patterns can you find?**

*(0, 5, 0, 5, in the thousandths place; 6 6, 7 7, 8 8, in the hundredths place)*

■ **What numbers would come next in the series if we continued adding 5 thousandths?**

*(.555, .560, .565, .570)*

■ **How would the pattern change if we added 10 thousandths or 1 hundredth each time?**

*(.560, .570, .580, .590)*

## Students subtract thousandths.

Be sure students have their desktop place value charts, scissors, and a large thousandths paper manipulative (made from Transparency 9A). Later, in this segment, you will need copies of *Worksheet 10B: Subtracting Thousandths* and a transparency of it for the overhead.

**We have been adding decimals for awhile. Now we are going to subtract decimals. Build 500 thousandths on your charts.**

■ **How do we do it?**

*(put 500 thousandths in the thousandths place, then regroup to 50 hundredths, then regroup to 5 tenths)*

**Let's subtract 9 thousandths from our 500 thousandths.**

Talk students through the process.

■ **How many thousandths do we have in our thousandths place?**

*(none)*

■ **How can we subtract 9 thousandths from none? What do we have to do?**

*(go to another place)*

■ **Can we go to the hundredths place?**

*(no)*

■ **Why not?**

*(there aren't any hundredths in the hundredths place)*

■ **Can we go to the tenths place?**

*(yes)*

**Let's cut up 1 of our tenths into 10 hundredths.**

■ **Where do we put these hundredths?**

*(in the hundredths place)*

■ **Now what do we have on our place value charts?**

*(4 tenths, 10 hundredths, 0 thousandths)*

■ **Can we subtract 9 thousandths, yet?**

*(no)*

■ **What do we have to do?**

*(cut up 1 of our hundredths into thousandths)*

■ **How many thousandths will that be?**

*(10)*

■ **Now what do we have on our place value charts?**

*(4 tenths, 9 hundredths and 10 thousandths)*

■ **If we take away 9 thousandths, what is left?**

*(491 thousandths)*

Put the transparency of *Worksheet 10B: Subtracting Thousandths* on the overhead and hand out copies to students. Point out that the algorithm in box 1 is the problem they just built on their charts. Review how to do this subtraction problem by relating the method of crossing out and changing numbers to the regrouping process that the students just completed on their charts.

**We started with 500 thousandths and wanted to subtract 9 thousandths, but we didn't have any thousandths in our number.**

■ **What regrouping did we have to do first?**

*(we had to trade 1 tenth for 10 hundredths)*

**We can show this on our worksheet by crossing out the 5 in the tenths place and writing 4 above it and then adding a 1 to the 0 in the hundredths place to show we now have 10 hundredths.**

■ **Could we subtract then?**

*(no)*

■ **What did we have to do next?**

*(trade 1 hundredth for 10 thousandths)*

We can show this on our worksheet by crossing out the 10 in the tenths place and writing 9 above it and then adding a 1 to the 0 in the thousandths place to show that we now have 10 thousandths.

■ **Did that give us enough thousandths to do the subtraction?**

*(yes)*

■ **What did we do next?**

*(subtracted 9 thousandths from 10 thousandths)*

■ **What did that leave us with?**

*(4 tenths, 9 hundredths, and 1 thousandth)*

■ **What is another way of saying that amount?**

*(491 thousandths)*

Have students notice that box 2 shows the algorithm for taking 9 more thousandths away from the previous answer. Before solving on paper, have students build the answer on their charts.

■ **How many thousandths do we have in the thousandths place?**

*(1 thousandth)*

■ **Can we take 9 thousandths away if we only have 1 thousandth in the thousandths place?**

*(no)*

■ **What must we do?**

*(see if we have any hundredths to make thousandths)*

■ **How many hundredths do we have?**

*(9)*

■ **What do we do next?**

*(take 1 hundredth and cut it up into 10 thousandths)*

■ **If we take away 9 thousandths, what do we have left?**

*(482 thousandths)*

**Recorders, solve the algorithm on your worksheets.**

Instruct students to continue building and recording to subtract 9 thousandths from each previous answer until they reach 320 thousandths, completing the worksheet.

*Regrouping decimal fractions in subtraction as well as addition on a place value chart gives students the opportunity to see addition and subtraction as inverse processes. It also reinforces the idea that regrouping in addition involves building groups of 10 whereas in subtraction regrouping involves breaking up groups of 10.*

*Students discover patterns and make predictions.*

Put a clean copy of *Transparency 10A: Decimal Patterns Ledger* on the overhead. Tell the students you are going to record their answers from *Worksheet 10B: Subtracting Thousandths*. Record the answers as students read outloud.

> Look at the numbers we have recorded on this ledger.

> ■ **What patterns can you find?**
>
> *(0, 1, 2, 3, . . ., in the thousandths place; 6 9, 8, 7, 6, in the hundredths place)*

> ■ **What numbers would come next in the series if we continued subtracting 9 thousandths?**
>
> *(.311, .302, .293, .284)*

> ■ **What would the pattern be if we subtracted 10 thousandths or 1 hundredth each time?**
>
> *(.310, .300, .290, .280)*

# Part II

# Real World Problems

*Students interpret sports data.*

Distribute the first page (Data) of *Worksheet 10C: Sports Problems* to each student and put a transparency of it on the overhead. (All three pages of Worksheet 10C will be used in the next segment.)

> We are going to use our decimal skills to solve real life story problems. But, first, let's make sure you understand the data on this sheet.

Write .250 on the chalkboard. Explain to students that a batting average of 250 means the batter makes a hit 250 times out of every thousand times at bat. Point out that people say 250, but it's written as 250 thousandths. The batting average is figured by dividing the number of hits by the number of times at bat.

> Look at the data on your sheet.

> ■ **Who has the best batting average and what is it?**
>
> *(Ty at .347)*

> ■ **Who has the worst batting average?**
>
> *(Joe at .198)*

> **Listed beside each weight lifter's name is the number of pounds they lifted.**

■ Who lifted the least number of pounds and how much was it?

*(Edwin, 1119.76 pounds)*

In the women's 100 meter backstroke there are two scores, one for each trial in their event.

■ Who swam the fastest in the first trial?

*(there was a tie between Lydia and June)*

■ How fast did they swim the 100 meter backstroke?

*(54.995)*

■ Was that fifty-four and nine hundred, ninety-five thousandths hours or minutes or seconds?

*(seconds)*

■ How many swimmers swam the 100 meters in less than 1 minute?

*(all of them)*

■ Who was the slowest swimmer in the Time Trial #1 of the Women's 400 Meter Run?

*(Michelle)*

■ What was her time?

*(59.014 seconds)*

■ Did Lisa win Time Trial #2 of the Women's 400 Meter Run?

*(no)*

Throughout the discussion emphasize that in some sports the winner has the highest number and in some sports the winner has the lowest number.

Let's look at the data for the Women's 400 Meter Run.

■ Would the winner be the person with the highest time score or the lowest time score?

*(lowest time)*

■ Who is the winner of the Time Trial #1 (400 Meter Run) and what was her time?

*(Lisa, 47.992 seconds)*

■ Did she run faster or slower in her Time Trial #2?

*(slower)*

■ Was that better or worse?

*(worse)*

In the swimming event, the swimmer with the highest score loses.

- **Who can explain why?**

  *(the higher the score the slower the swimmer)*

- **Name the events or activities on our data sheet where the best have the highest scores?**

  *(batting average, weight lifting)*

## *Students subtract decimal fractions.*

Students continue to work with just the first page (Data) of *Worksheet 10C: Sports Problems* but will need all three pages at the end of this segment. Divide students into pairs.

> **Let's look at the Women's 100 Meter Backstroke trials on the data sheet. Donna improved her time during the second trial by a very small fraction of a second. Work with your partner to write and solve the problem to figure out how much Donna improved.**

Give students a few minutes to work together, then go through the process with them.

- **May I have a volunteer come up and write the problem on the overhead or chalkboard?**

  *(student writes:)*

  $$\begin{array}{r} 56.793 \\ -56.659 \\ \hline \end{array}$$

- **What do we have to do in order to find the difference in time that Donna took to swim each lap?**

  *(subtract)*

- **How much did Donna improve her time on the second trial?**

  *(134 thousandths of a second)*

> **Let's look again at the data for the Women's 100 Meter Backstroke. Now let's compare Marilyn's first and second trials. Note that she also improved her speed. Work with your partner to write and solve the problem to figure out how much she improved.**

Then review the process with students by having a volunteer solve the problem and explain the procedure, step-by-step. Be sure students include the unit of measure (seconds, pounds) when expressing the answers.

Distribute pages 2 and 3 of Worksheet 10C to each student. Have them work individually or in pairs to complete it.

## Part III

# Adding and Subtracting Mixed Numbers with Decimal Dough

*Re-introduce Decimal Dough and review whole number regrouping.*

Distribute desktop place value charts. Make decimal dough from *Manipulatives 5A: Decimal Dough Bills; Manipulatives 10A: Decimal Dough Coins.* Distribute to each student 20 of each of the following Decimal Dough denominations: hundreds, tens, ones, dimes, pennies, and mills.

Tell students they will again be using Decimal Dough (introduced in Unit Five). Previously, however, they only worked with whole number dough or bills.

> **Today your dough includes dimes, pennies or cents, and a new denomination called mills. When we talk about money we usually say' dollars and cents. Remember 1 penny is the same as 1 cent.**

- **How many dimes equals 1 dollar?**

    *(10)*

> **Correct. So 1 dime is 1 tenth of 1 dollar. That's why it says .1 on our Decimal Dough dimes.**

- **How many pennies equal 1 dollar?**

    *(100)*

> **Correct. So 1 penny is 1 hundredth of 1 dollar. That's why it says .01 on our Decimal Dough pennies.**

Explain to students that in our Decimal Dough system we have a new denomination called a mill. Explain that mills are the denomination used to figure property tax. There are 1000 mills in 1 dollar.

- **What does it say on our mills coins?**

    *(.001)*

- **Who can tell us why?**

    *(because 1 mill is 1 thousandth of 1 dollar)*

Tell students you are going to review regrouping, for a few minutes, with just their whole number dough.

> **Place 9 dollars on your place value chart. Then, add 1 more dollar.**

- **What must we do?**

    *(trade in the 10 one-dollars for 1 ten-dollar and put it in the tens place)*

■ **If we add 9 more tens, what must we do?**

*(trade in the 10 ten-dollars for 1 hundred-dollar and put it in the hundreds place)*

Make sure students are comfortable building and regrouping Decimal Dough dollars before moving on to coins.

## Students add mixed numbers with Decimal Dough.

Continuing from the previous segment, make sure students still have 1 hundred-dollar bill on their place value charts.

■ **What place is to the right of the decimal point?**

*(tenths)*

■ **What coin represents 1 tenth of a dollar?**

*(dime)*

■ **Why does 1 dime equal 1 tenth?**

*(because there are 10 dimes in 1 dollar and there are 10 tenths in 1 whole)*

■ **Add 5 tenths. What do we have now?**

*(1 hundred and 5 tenths or 100 dollars and 50 cents)*

■ **If we add 6 dimes or 60 cents, what must we do?**

*(trade 10 dimes for 1 dollar and put it in the ones place)*

■ **How much money do we have now?**

*(101 dollars and 10 cents)*

■ **What's another way to read that number?**

*(101 and 1 tenth dollars)*

Check to see that each student has 1 hundred-dollar bill, 1 one-dollar bill, and 1 dime in the correct place on the chart.

■ **What place is to the right of the tenths place?**

*(hundredths)*

■ **What coin represents 1 hundredth of a dollar?**

*(penny)*

■ **Why does a penny equal 1 hundredth?**

*(because there are 100 pennies in 1 dollar and there are 100 hundredths in 1 whole)*

■ **What is another name for a penny?**

*(cent)*

■ **What does a cent equal?**

*(1 hundredth of a dollar)*

■ **How many pennies equal a dime?**

*(10)*

■ **How many hundredths equal 1 tenth?**

*(10)*

Students should still have 101.1 built on their charts.

**Add 7 cents or 7 hundredths.**

■ **How much do we have now?**

*(101 dollars and 17 cents, or 101 and 17 hundredths dollars)*

■ **To add 9 more cents, what must we do?**

*(trade in 10 pennies for 1 dime and put it in the tenths place)*

■ **How much money do we have now?**

*(101 dollars and 26 cents)*

■ **What is another way to read that amount?**

*(101 and 26 hundredths dollars)*

Stress that pennies are hundredths of dollars and dimes are tenths of dollars. Discuss the relationship of pennies to hundredths, pennies to dimes, and hundredths to tenths. Be sure students have 101.26 built correctly on their place value charts. Then continue.

■ **What place is to the right of the hundredths place?**

*(thousandths)*

■ **What coin represents 1 thousandth of a dollar?**

*(mill)*

■ **Why does 1 mill equal 1 thousandth?**

*(because there are 1000 mills in 1 dollar and there are 1000 thousandths in 1 whole)*

■ **How many mills equal a penny?**

*(10)*

■ **How many mills equal 1 hundredth?**

*(10)*

**Now let's add 8 mills.**

■ **How much do we have now?**

*(101 dollars, 2 dimes, 6 pennies, and 8 mills; 101 dollars and 268 mills; 101 and 268 thousandths dollars)*

■ **If we add 7 more mills, what must we do?**

*(trade in 10 mills for 1 penny and put it in the hundredths place)*

■ **How much money do we have now?**

*(101 dollars and 275 mills.)*

■ **What is another way to read that amount?**

*(101 and 275 thousandths dollars)*

Give the students more problems regrouping mills, emphasizing that mills are thousandths of dollars.

## Emphasize Decimal Dough equivalents.

Continue counting and regrouping activities with place value charts and Decimal Dough. Have students help create the following table on the chalkboard:

| | |
|---|---|
| 10 mills | = 1 penny |
| 10 pennies | = 1 dime |
| 10 dimes | = 1 dollar |
| 10 dollars | = 1 ten-dollar bill |
| 10 ten-dollar bills | = 1 hundred-dollar bill |

Elicit more student help to create the following:

| | | |
|---|---|---|
| 1 mill | = 1 thousandth | |
| 10 mills | = 1 penny | = 1 hundredth |
| 10 pennies | = 1 dime | = 1 tenth, or 10 hundredths |
| 10 dimes | = 1 dollar | = 1 whole, or 10 tenths |

## Students shade and build decimal fractions.

Distribute to each student desktop place value charts and 20 each of the following Decimal Dough denominations: hundreds, tens, ones, dimes, pennies, and mills. Have available copies of *Worksheet 9A: Counting Squares—Thousandths.* Put a transparency of it on the overhead with the following amounts already shaded: .835, .023, .46 and .909. Cut up *Transparency 10B: Decimal Dough Coins for Overhead,* so you have coins for the overhead.

**Look at the first counting square on the overhead.**

■ **Who can tell me the amount that is shaded?**

*(835 thousandths)*

■ **How many mills is that?**

*(835 mills)*

Have students use their Decimal Dough to build .835 on their charts. Then continue the same procedure with each of other three numbers that are shaded on the transparency.

Next, reverse the procedure. Remove the shaded transparency from the overhead and show the following transparency coins: 4 dimes, 3 pennies, and 6 mills. Hand out paper copies of *Worksheet 9A: Counting Squares—Thousandths* to the students. Direct attention to the overhead.

> **This time we are going to shade our counting squares on our worksheets to represent amounts of money. Let's pretend this is the change from my pocket.**

- **How much Decimal Dough do I have?**

  *(436 mills; 436 thousandths of a dollar; almost 44 cents)*

Instruct the students to shade in the first counting square on their worksheet to represent that amount of money. Then add 3 dimes, 6 pennies and 3 mills to the amount already on the overhead.

> **I found some more change and now I have 7 dimes, 9 pennies and 9 mills altogether.**

- **How can we shade the second counting square to show the amount of change I now have?**

  *(shade in 799 thousandths)*

- **How much money do I have now?**

  *(799 mills; 799 thousandths of a dollar; a little more than 79 cents)*

Be sure that students read the number in different ways. This helps them see the relationship between tenths and dimes, hundredths and pennies, and thousandths and mills. Then continue by clearing the overhead and putting out 7 dimes and 2 pennies.

> **I was so hungry that I went to the store and spent 72 cents on candy. Shade in the third counting square to show the amount of Decimal Dough I spent.**

- **What did you shade on your worksheet?**

  *(72 hundredths)*

- **Why did you shade in 72 hundredths?**

  *(because 72 cents is the same as 72 hundredths of a dollar)*

- **How many thousandths equals 72 hundredths?**

  *(720)*

Again, clear the overhead and put 4 dimes on it.

> **Let's try one more. On the sidewalk I found 4 dimes. Shade in the last counting square to show the amount of money I found.**

- **What did you shade in on your worksheet?**

  *(4 tenths)*

- **Why did you shade in 4 tenths?**

  *(because 4 dimes is the same as 4 tenths of a dollar or 40 cents)*

# Part IV

# Problem-Solving with Counting Squares and Decimal Dough

## *Students shade to represent mixed numbers and solve problems.*

Distribute *Worksheet 10D: Counting Squares for Mixed Numbers* and three different color crayons to each student. Put a transparency of Worksheet 10D on the overhead. Explain to students that you are going to tell them a story that uses mixed numbers.

■ **Who can define or give me an example of a mixed number?**

*(mixed number combines a whole number and a part of a whole; 2 and 2 tenths; 2.2; 2 2/10)*

**A few years ago my friend had a daughter who was born prematurely. The little girl, named Elizabeth, only weighed 2 and 35 hundredths pounds when she was born.**

Instruct the students to use the first row of counting squares on their worksheet to shade in Elizabeth's birth weight with a colored crayon. Do the same on the transparency after students finish.

**The doctors told my friend that she couldn't hold her baby until Elizabeth weighed 3 lb. My friend called the intensive care unit at the hospital every day to find out if Elizabeth had put on any weight.**

■ **Does anyone know how much weight Elizabeth had to gain to reach 3 pounds?**

*(students respond)*

If students answered the question above correctly, then use the following to prove the answer. If they cannot answer it, then use the following to guide them through the process to find the answer.

Instruct students to use a second color crayon and continue shading the counting squares in the first row until they reach 3 pounds. Then demonstrate on the transparency.

■ **What amount did you shade with the second color?**

*(65 hundredths)*

■ **65 hundredths of what? An ounce? A pound?**

*(65 hundredths of a pound)*

■ **What amount does one shaded square represent?**

*(1 pound)*

■ **Two shaded squares? Three?**

*(2 pounds; 3 pounds)*

Point out to students they can also answer this problem using subtraction. Ask a volunteer to write and solve the arithmetic problem on the chalkboard.

$$\begin{array}{r} 3.00 \\ -\ 2.35 \\ \hline .65 \end{array}$$

Then continue with the story.

> When Elizabeth reached 3 pounds, her mother was very happy to be able to hold her. Naturally, she wanted to take Elizabeth home. But the hospital said she couldn't take her daughter home until Elizabeth weighed 4 and 5 tenths pounds.

Have students use their third color crayon and draw a circle around a total of 4 and 5 tenths in the first row, making sure to include the three counting squares already shaded. Then demonstrate on the transparency.

■ **How much weight did she need to gain?**

*(1.5 pounds)*

Point out that the three shaded counting squares show Elizabeth's present weight. Explain that the unshaded area represents the weight Elizabeth needs to gain before being allowed to go home. Ask students to write and solve the algorithm.

$$\begin{array}{r} 4.50 \\ -3.00 \\ \hline \end{array}$$

Continue with a new problem.

> My two sisters and I wanted to buy a jumbo size box of popcorn to munch on during a movie. It cost 2 dollars and 59 cents, including tax. None of us had enough after we purchased our movie tickets so we had to pool our money. I had 1 dollar and 1 tenth.

Instruct students to use the second row of squares on their worksheet and color in 1 dollar and 1 tenth. Demonstrate on the transparency. Stress that the number can be thought of as 1 dollar and 1 tenth of a dollar or 1 dollar and 10 cents.

> My sister Elaine had 99 hundredths. Continue with the squares in the second row. Use another color to shade in 99 hundredths.

Make sure students see the relationship between 99 hundredths and 99 cents.

■ **How much money do Elaine and I have altogether?**

*(2 dollars and 9 cents)*

■ **Do the two of us have enough money to buy the popcorn?**

*(no)*

Ask a volunteer to set up and prove the answer arithmetically on the chalkboard:

$$\begin{array}{r} 1.10 \\ +\ .99 \\ \hline 2.09 \end{array}$$

Lucky for us, another sister came with us to the movies. Vickie had 590 mills.

- **How many thousandths is 590 mills?**

  *(590)*

- **How many hundredths is 590 thousandths?**

  *(59)*

Instruct students to continue using the squares in the second row and use another color to shade in 590 thousandths or 59 hundredths. Students can choose which to shade.

- **How much money do the three of us have altogether?**

  *(2 dollars and 680 mills)*

- **Do we have enough money to buy the popcorn?**

  *(yes)*

Ask a volunteer to set up and prove the answer arithmetically on the chalkboard:

$$\begin{array}{r} 2.090 \\ +\ .590 \\ \hline 2.680 \text{ or } \$2.68 \end{array}$$

Direct the students to use the last row of counting squares to solve the next problem.

> **Last week my sister Vickie went to the store and bought some fruit. Vickie bought 1 and 69 hundredths pounds of cherries and 2 and 35 hundredths pounds of bananas. How much fruit did Vickie buy altogether?**

To do this problem, have students shade in the amount of cherries Vickie bought using one color and the amount of bananas Vickie bought using another color.

> **After you finish shading to show the answer, write and solve the problem on the back of the worksheet.**

$$\begin{array}{l} 1.65 \\ \underline{2.35} \\ 4.00 \text{ pounds of fruit} \end{array}$$

If students need additional practice, distribute a second copy of Worksheet 10D and have students suggest possible story problems for the class to shade and solve.

# Part V

# Reinforcement Activities

## *Activity 1: Robo-Batter*

This activity involves ordering, comparing, and computing decimals. Students may work individually or in pairs. Distribute the first page (Data) of *Worksheet 10C: Sports Problems* and *Worksheet 10E: Robo-Batter* to each student. Students use the data to solve the problems.

## Activity 2: Decimal Dough Story Problems

Organize students into pairs or small groups. Distribute desktop place value charts and 12 each of the following denominations: ones, tens, dimes, pennies, and mills.

Give each student a copy of *Worksheet 10F: Decimal Dough Story Problems.* Students work together to build the number on the place value chart and answer the questions.

## Activity 3: Checkbook Problems

Organize students into pairs and distribute *Worksheet 10G: Checkbook Problems.* Page 1 of the worksheet describes eight money transactions. Page 2 of the worksheet is a ledger sheet. One student reads each step while the other student computes the problem and records the new balance on the ledger sheet. Students should change roles after the first four steps.

## Activity 4: Kingdom of Wize

Students may work individually or in pairs. Distribute *Worksheet 10H: Kingdom of Wize Problems.* Students solve application problems involving area, average family income, and annual snowfall in the mythical kingdom.

# Part VI

# Assessment Opportunities

This unit contains opportunities for both informal and formal assessment. Using the sports data, working with Decimal Dough, and doing the Reinforcement Activities in this unit require students to apply their knowledge of decimals in problem-solving situations. Constructing and regrouping thousandths on the desktop place value chart requires students to demonstrate their understanding of decimal equivalences and the grouping and trading rules which characterize the system. Any of the worksheets, if completed independently, could be used as formal assessments.

Finally, the decimal pretests *(Assessment 6A: Decimal Concepts* and *Assessment 6B: Decimal Applications)* can be administered as post-assessments. Comparing student performance before and after instruction provides an opportunity to measure student growth across all concepts.

# BLACKLINE MASTERS

**Name:** _____        **Date:** _____

# Whole Numbers

Directions: These problems will be read aloud and you will be given time to solve them. You will not receive a grade on this test.

## Part One: Multiple Choice

Read each answer carefully and then *circle the letter* of the most appropriate choice.

1. Which numeral is equivalent to 4 tens, 9 ones, 2 hundreds?
   a. Not given      b. 249       c. 942       d. 294       e. I don't know.

2. Which numeral stands for 3 thousands, 5 ones, 4 hundreds, 8 tens?
   a. Not given      b. 3548      c. 3845      d. 3458      e. I don't know.

3. Which numeral stands for 5 ones, 4 thousands, 5 hundreds?
   a. Not given      b. 545       c. 455       d. 4505      e. I don't know.

4. Which of the choices below is equivalent to 574?
   a. Not given      b. 5 hundreds, 4 ones    c. 5 hundreds, 47 tens
   d. 57 tens, 4 ones             e. 50 tens, 4 ones

5. Which number is equivalent to 2000 − 20?
   a. Not given      b.1980       c. 18,080   d. 1990       e. I don't know.

## Part Two: Fill in the blank

Read the questions and write the answers in the blanks provided.

6. What numeral is equivalent to 2 tens, 9 hundreds, 7 ones?

   _____

7. I have 4 tens, 2 thousands, 8 ones, 3 hundreds. What number do I have?  Write it in the space below.

   _____

8. I have 1 ten, 8 thousands, 0 hundreds, 6 ones. What number do I have? Write it in the space below.

   _____

9. I have 2 ones, 1 ten, and 5 thousands. What number do I have? Write it in the space below.

   _____

**Name:** _____     **Date:** _____

10. 36 tens is equal to

_____

11. 2 tens + 47 ones equals

_____

12. 3 thousands + 15 hundreds + 1 ten equals

_____

13. Write in numerals: three thousands, seven ones

_____

14. Write the number this picture represents.

_____

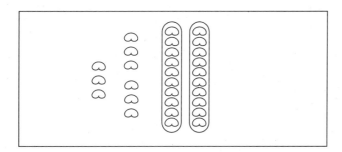

15. Write the number this picture represents.

_____

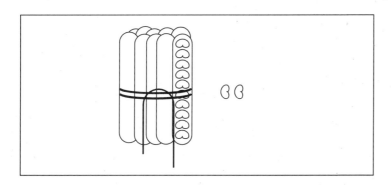

# Whole Numbers Applications

Directions: Your teacher will read the test aloud as you solve the problems. You will not
receive a grade on this test.

1. Sam had 595 postage stamps in his collection while Lisa had 624 stamps. If they put
   their stamp collections together, then how many stamps would they have in all? *Write
   the problem and solve it.*

2. How many more stamps does Lisa have than Sam? *Write the problem and solve it.*

3. Maria received several birthday checks from relatives for the following amounts: $27,
   $45, $99, $101, $28. How much money did she receive in all? *Write the problem and
   solve it.*

4.  Some engineers in Michigan earn $45,276 a year. Engineers in another state with the same number of years' experience and level of education would make $36,891. How much more does the engineer in Michigan earn than the engineer in the other state? *Write the problem and solve it.*

5.  Brad, a middle school student, buys hot lunch at school every day. This costs him $2.00 per day.

    a. How much would Brad pay for a week of school lunches?

    _____

    b. How much would five students pay altogether for a week of lunches?

    _____

    c. How much would it cost five students to eat lunch every day for 2 weeks?

    _____

6.  If you paid for 50 school lunches with a thousand dollar bill, how much money would you get as change? *Write the problem and solve it.*

# Large Counting Squares

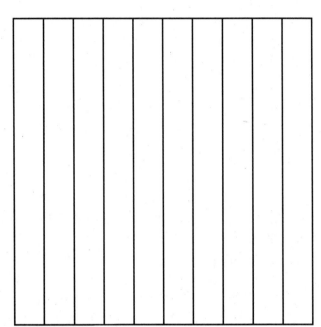
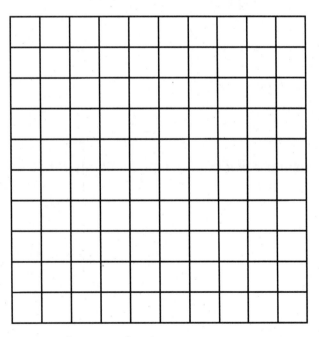
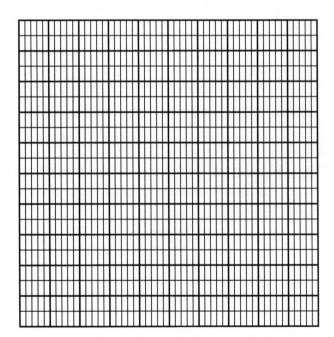

# Small Counting Squares

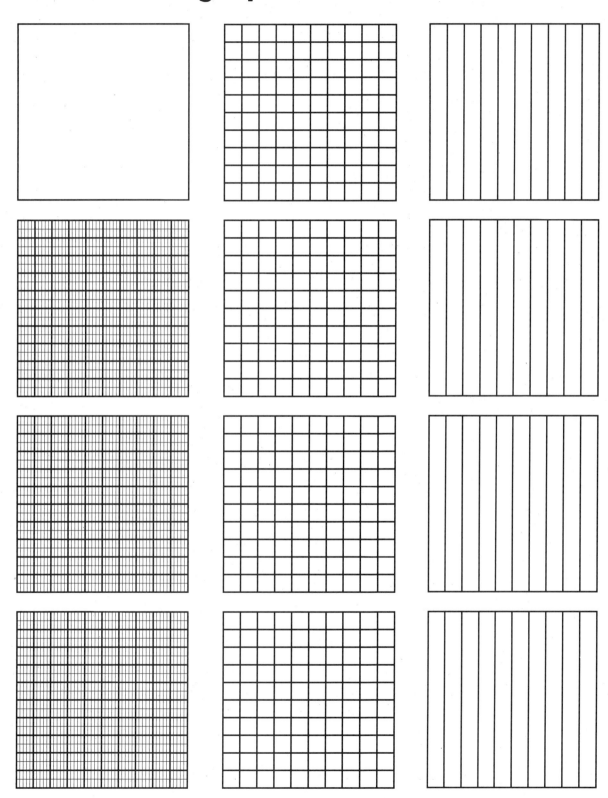

**Name:** _____          **Date:** _____

# Show Your Age

Directions: Do these constructions with a partner.

1. Build your age. Combine it with your partner's age.

   How many tens did you use?          _____

   How many ones did you use?          _____

   Did you have to regroup?            _____

   What were your combined ages?  _____

2. Build the age of one of your parents. Combine it with the age of your partner's parent.

   How many tens did you use?          _____

   How many ones did you use?          _____

   Did you have to regroup?            _____

   What were your parents'
   combined ages?                      _____

3. Combine the ages of three people of your choice.

   How many tens did you use?          _____

   How many ones did you use?          _____

   Did you have to regroup?            _____

   What was the total of the
   three people's ages combined?   _____

**Name:** _____          **Date:** _____

# Value of Digits

1. In the number 9731, the digit "9" has the greatest value. What is its value?

   _____

2. Take the following digits: 0 3 7 5
   Order them to create the largest number.

   _____

3. What is the number that is 1 less than 1000?

   _____

4. If I removed both zeros from the number 9009 what number would I have?

   _____

5. What does the zero stand for in the number 3086?

   _____

6. Write the number that is made up of: 5 ones, 6 tens, 7 hundreds, and 8 thousands.

   _____

7. Take the following digits: 2 9 1 5
   Order them to create the smallest number.

   _____

**Name:** _____     **Date:** _____

# Catalogue Shopping

Directions: Using the catalogue price list below, answer the following questions. Build and solve the problems with your desktop place value chart and counting squares.

| | | | |
|---|---|---|---|
| Boom box | $ 139 | Jeans | $ 51 |
| Dirt bike | $ 111 | Sweater | $ 76 |
| Video game cartridge | $ 42 | Watch | $ 26 |
| Backpack | $ 12 | Skis | $ 285 |
| Cross-training shoes | $ 95 | Tennis racket | $ 107 |

1. What is the combined total of all the clothes listed on your catalogue price list?

   _____

2. What is the combined total of the skis, tennis racket, and backpack on your catalogue price list?

   _____

3. If you bought the 3 most expensive items on the list, how much would you spend?

   _____

4. How much would the 3 least expensive items on the catalogue list cost?

   _____

5. If you had $100, could you buy the video cartridge, the backpack, and the jeans?

   Yes _____ No _____

        

**Name:** _____          **Date:** _____

# Flexible Regrouping

Directions: Read and answer each of the problems.
            Reorder the digits, if necessary. Regroup the quantities if you must.
            Then build the number on the place value chart.

1.  Tim wanted to buy his mother a new vacuum cleaner for Christmas. He saved all
    of his money from his paper route for a whole year and had 11 ten-dollar bills and
    20 one-dollar bills. The vacuum cleaner cost $119. Did he have enough money?
    How much money did Tim have?

    a. _____          b. _____

2.  Sally has $226 in the bank.

    If she went to the bank and asked for the $226 in tens and ones, what would the bank
    likely give her?

    _____ Tens                _____Ones

3.  If she wanted to get her $226 in one-dollar bills only, how many one-dollar bills would
    the bank give her?

    _____ Ones

4.  If she wanted to get her money in hundred-dollar bills, how many hundred-dollar bills
    would the bank give her?

    _____ Hundreds

5.  How much would the bank still owe her?

    _____Tens                _____Ones

**Name:** _____

**Date:** _____

# Numbers Out of Sequence

Directions: Using your place value chart and counting squares, build each number.

1. 2 tens          0 hundreds       5 ones
   Build.
   Write the number. _____

2. 6 ones         2 hundreds       3 tens
   Build.
   Write the number. _____

3. 9 ones         1 hundred        9 tens
   Build.
   Write the number. _____

4. 1 hundred       1 one            8 tens
   Build.
   Write the number. _____

5. 4 tens         0 hundreds       0 ones
   Build.
   Write the number. _____

6. 2 ones         11 tens
   Build.
   Write the number. _____

7. 12 tens        2 ones        1 hundred
   Build.
   Write the number. _____

8. 30 ones       1 ten          2 hundreds
   Build.
   Write the number. _____

9. 16 ones       2 tens        2 hundreds
   Build.
   Write the number. _____

10. Three children were weighed at the clinic. One child weighed 20 pounds, another child weighed 57 pounds, and the third child weighed 22 pounds. What was their total weight? *Set up a problem and solve.*

11. Using your answer from #10 above, find out how far their total weight is from 100 pounds. *Set up a problem and solve.*

# Digit Cards

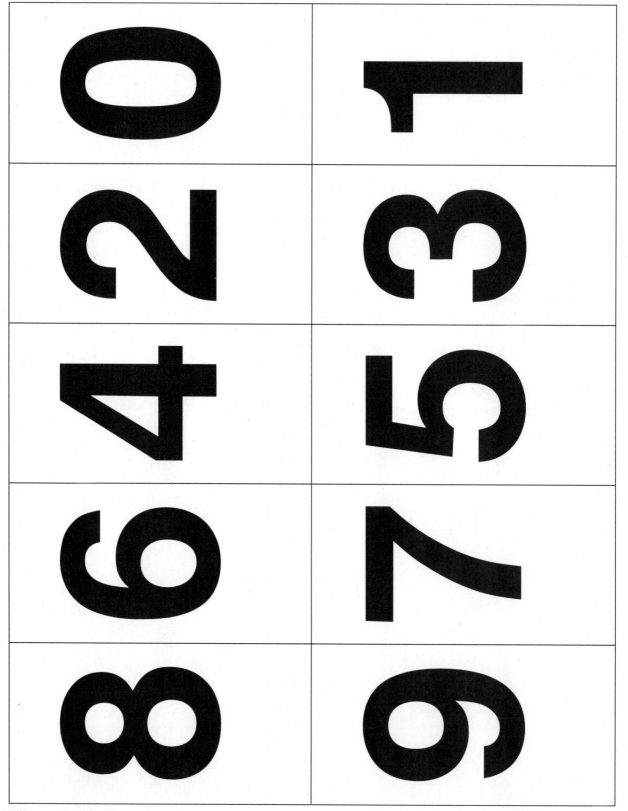

**Name:** _____　　**Date:** _____

# Addition Recording Sheet

|  |  |  |  |  |
|---|---|---|---|---|
| 0<br>+ 0<br>―――<br>0 | 0<br>+ 5<br>―――<br>5 | ☐<br>+ 5<br>――― | ☐<br>+ 5<br>――― | ☐<br>+ 5<br>――― |
| ☐<br>+ 5<br>――― | ☐<br>+ 5<br>――― | 30<br>+ 5<br>――― | ☐<br>+ 5<br>――― | ☐<br>+ 5<br>――― |
| 45<br>+ 5<br>――― | ☐<br>+ 5<br>――― | ☐<br>+ 5<br>――― | 60<br>+ 5<br>――― | ☐<br>+ 5<br>――― |
| ☐<br>+ 5<br>――― | ☐<br>+ 5<br>――― | ☐<br>+ 5<br>――― | 85<br>+ 5<br>――― | ☐<br>+ 5<br>――― |
| ☐<br>+ 5<br>――― | 100<br>+ 5<br>――― | ☐<br>+ 5<br>――― | ☐<br>+ 5<br>――― | ☐<br>+ 5<br>――― |

　　　　　　　　　　　　　　　　　BLACKLINE MASTERS　**137**

**Name:** _____      **Date:** _____

# Patterns of Five Ledger

| Hundreds | Tens | Ones |
|---|---|---|

$0 + 0$  =  _____0_____

$0 + 5$  =  _____

$5 + 5$  =  _____

$10 + 5$  =  _____

$15 + 5$  =  _____

$20 + 5$  =  _____

$25 + 5$  =  _____

$30 + 5$  =  _____

$35 + 5$  =  _____

$40 + 5$  =  _____

$45 + 5$  =  _____

$50 + 5$  =  _____

$55 + 5$  =  _____

**Name:** _____

**Date:** _____

|  | Hundreds | Tens | Ones |
|---|---|---|---|
| 60 + 5 = _____ | _____ | _____ | _____ |
| 65 + 5 = _____ | _____ | _____ | _____ |
| 70 + 5 = _____ | _____ | _____ | _____ |
| 75 + 5 = _____ | _____ | _____ | _____ |
| 80 + 5 = _____ | _____ | _____ | _____ |
| 85 + 5 = _____ | _____ | _____ | _____ |
| 90 + 5 = _____ | _____ | _____ | _____ |
| 95 + 5 = _____ | _____ | _____ | _____ |
| 100 + 5 = _____ | _____ | _____ | _____ |
| 105 + 5 = _____ | _____ | _____ | _____ |
| 110 + 5 = _____ | _____ | _____ | _____ |
| 115 + 5 = _____ | _____ | _____ | _____ |

**Name:** _____        **Date:** _____

# Subtraction Recording Sheet

| 120 | 119 | ☐ | ☐ | ☐ |
|---|---|---|---|---|
| −1 | −1 | −1 | −1 | −1 |

| ☐ | ☐ | 113 | ☐ | ☐ |
|---|---|---|---|---|
| −1 | −1 | −1 | −1 | −1 |

| 110 | ☐ | ☐ | ☐ | ☐ |
|---|---|---|---|---|
| −1 | −1 | −1 | −1 | −1 |
| | | | | 105 |

| 105 | ☐ | ☐ | ☐ | ☐ |
|---|---|---|---|---|
| −5 | −5 | −5 | −5 | −5 |

| 80 | ☐ | ☐ | ☐ | ☐ |
|---|---|---|---|---|
| −5 | −5 | −5 | −5 | −5 |

| ☐ |
|---|
| −5 |

                                 

**Name:** _____

**Date:** _____

# Addition and Subtraction Recording Sheet

|  50 | □ | □ | □ | □ |
| --- | --- | --- | --- | --- |
| −3 | +7 | +8 | −23 | +30 |

| □ | □ | □ | | |
| --- | --- | --- | --- | --- |
| +31 | −11 | +22 | _____ | _____ |

_____  _____  _____  _____  _____

_____  _____  _____  _____  _____

_____  _____  _____  _____  _____

**Name:** _____          **Date:** _____

# Shopping List Problems

| Item | Description | Price |
|------|-------------|-------|
| A | Skateboard | $35. |
| B | Perfume | $ 8. |
| C | Basketball | $17. |
| D | Blouse | $24. |
| E | Bike | $110. |
| F | Brush | $ 2. |
| G | Cross-training Shoes | $73. |
| H | Colored Markers | $ 5. |
| I | Pistons' Tickets | $49. |
| J | Flowers | $13. |
| K | Candy Bar | $1. |
| L | Camera | $62. |
| M | Video Game | $27. |
| N | Yearbook | $16. |
| O | Video Rental | $ 3. |
| P | Nail Polish | $ 1. |
| Q | Compact Disc | $11. |
| R | In-line skates | $99. |
| S | Concert Tickets | $58. |
| T | Airplane Ticket | $882. |

**Name:** _____          **Date:** _____

Directions: Solve the shopping list problems. Show your work below each problem.

1.   How much would it cost to buy item G and item C?

   _____

2.   How much money would you need to buy items T, S, and J? Prove this on your place value chart.

   _____

3.   What is the greatest number of items you could buy from the list if you started with 200 dollars?

   _____

4.   How many video games could you buy if you had 100 dollars? How much money would you have left over?

   _____

**Name:** _____          **Date:** _____

Directions: Solve the shopping list problems. Show your work below each problem.

5.    You went to the store with 100 dollars. First you bought item P, then you went to
      another store and bought item L. How much did you have left?

      _____

6.    How much less is item Q than item E?

      _____

7.    How much would it cost to buy everything you can wear from the list?

      _____

8.    How much would it cost to buy all the items that are used for travel?

      _____

# Whole Numbers for Human Place Value Chart

# ones

# tens

# hundreds

# Whole Numbers for Human Place Value Chart

# thousands

# ten thousands

# hundred thousands

# Whole Numbers for Human Place Value Chart

# millions

# ten millions

# hundred millions

**Name:** _____          **Date:** _____

| Name: _____ |
| :--- |
| Date: _____ |
| **Hundreds Ledger** |

| Hundreds | Tens | Ones |
| --- | --- | --- |
|  |  |  |
|  |  |  |
|  |  |  |
|  |  |  |
|  |  |  |
|  |  |  |
|  |  |  |
|  |  |  |
|  |  |  |
|  |  |  |

| Name: _____ |
| :--- |
| Date: _____ |
| **Hundreds Ledger** |

| Hundreds | Tens | Ones |
| --- | --- | --- |
|  |  |  |
|  |  |  |
|  |  |  |
|  |  |  |
|  |  |  |
|  |  |  |
|  |  |  |
|  |  |  |
|  |  |  |
|  |  |  |

**Name:** _____        **Date:** _____

| Name: _____ |
| :-- |

Name: _____

Date: _____

## Thousands Ledger

| Thousands | Hundreds | Tens | Ones |
| --- | --- | --- | --- |
| | | | |
| | | | |
| | | | |
| | | | |
| | | | |
| | | | |
| | | | |
| | | | |
| | | | |
| | | | |
| | | | |

Name: _____

Date: _____

## Thousands Ledger

| Thousands | Hundreds | Tens | Ones |
| --- | --- | --- | --- |
| | | | |
| | | | |
| | | | |
| | | | |
| | | | |
| | | | |
| | | | |
| | | | |
| | | | |
| | | | |
| | | | |

**Name:** _____     **Date:** _____

# Flexible Regrouping

1. 10 ones = 1 _____

2. 10 hundreds = 1 _____

3. 10 tens = 1 _____

4. Write 5,642 in four different ways to demonstrate flexible grouping.

   5,642 = _____ thousands, _____ hundreds, _____ tens, _____ ones

   OR _____ hundreds, _____ tens, _____ ones

   OR _____ tens, _____ ones

   OR _____ ones

5. Write 6,002 in four different ways to demonstrate flexible grouping.

   6,002 = _____ thousands, _____ hundreds, _____ tens, _____ ones

   OR _____ hundreds, _____ tens, _____ ones

   OR _____ tens, _____ ones

   OR _____ ones

6. Explain why 4,294 can also be thought of as 42 hundreds, 9 tens, and 4 ones.

   _____

   _____

   _____

   _____

   _____

# Decimal Dough Bills

| | |
|---|---|
| $1 | $1 |
| $1 | $1 |
| $1 | $1 |
| $1 | $1 |

# Decimal Dough Bills

| | |
|---|---|
| **$10** | **$10** |
| **$10** | **$10** |
| **$10** | **$10** |
| **$10** | **$10** |

# Decimal Dough Bills

| | |
|---|---|
| $100 | $100 |
| $100 | $100 |
| $100 | $100 |
| $100 | $100 |

# Decimal Dough Bills

| | |
|---|---|
| $1,000 | $1,000 |
| $1,000 | $1,000 |
| $1,000 | $1,000 |
| $1,000 | $1,000 |

# Decimal Dough Bills

| | |
|:---:|:---:|
| **$10,000** | **$10,000** |
| **$10,000** | **$10,000** |
| **$10,000** | **$10,000** |
| **$10,000** | **$10,000** |

# Decimal Dough Bills

| | |
|---|---|
| **$100,000** | **$100,000** |
| **$100,000** | **$100,000** |
| **$100,000** | **$100,000** |
| **$100,000** | **$100,000** |

# Decimal Dough Bills

| | |
|---|---|
| **$1,000,000** | **$1,000,000** |
| **$1,000,000** | **$1,000,000** |
| **$1,000,000** | **$1,000,000** |
| **$1,000,000** | **$1,000,000** |

**Name:** _____

**Date:** _____

# Tally Sheet

|  | Number of Each | Subtotal |
|---|---|---|
| Ten Thousands | | |
| Thousands | | |
| Hundreds | | |
| Tens | | |
| Ones | | |

Total:_____

|  | Number of Each | Subtotal |
|---|---|---|
| Ten Thousands | | |
| Thousands | | |
| Hundreds | | |
| Tens | | |
| Ones | | |

Total:_____

|  | Number of Each | Subtotal |
|---|---|---|
| Ten Thousands | | |
| Thousands | | |
| Hundreds | | |
| Tens | | |
| Ones | | |

Total:_____

**Name:** _____

**Date:** _____

# Decimal Concepts

Directions: These questions will be read aloud and you will have time to answer them. You will not receive a grade on this test.

1.  If this unit = 1, then which picture below shows 2.3?
    (Circle the letter of the correct answer.)

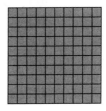

a.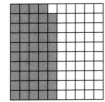

b.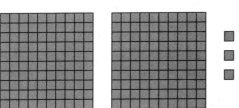

c.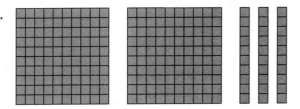

d.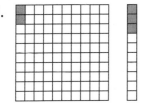

e. Not given

f. I don't know.

**Name:** _____     **Date:** _____

2. If this unit = 1,

then write the number that is represented by

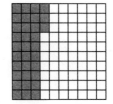

_____

3. Shade in the counting square to equal the number .7

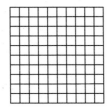

4. Shade in the counting square to equal the number .07

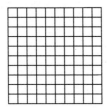

5. Shade in the counting square to equal the number .75

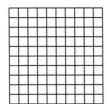

**Name:** _____       **Date:** _____

6. Shade .6 of this figure:

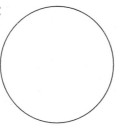

Circle the letter of the correct answer.

7. Which is the largest number?

    a. 5.6      b. 5.495      c. 5.4379      d. 5.0004      e. I don't know.

8. Which is the smallest number?

    a. 7.145    b. 7.3      c. 7.91      d. 7.015      e. I don't know.

9. Which of the choices below represents 305 thousandths?

    a. 3.05      b. .035      c. .305      d. .3005      e. I don't know.

10. Which of the choices below represents thirty-nine hundredths?

    a. 3900      b. 390.0      c. 0.039      d. 0.39      e. I don't know.

11. Which of the choices below represents five and fourteen thousandths?

    a. .514      b. 5.014      c. 5.140      d. .0514      e. I don't know.

12. Which of the choices below represents one tenth?

    a. .1      b. .01      c. .001      d. .0010      e. I don't know.

13. Write fifty-seven hundredths in numerals on the line below.

_____

14. Write four tenths in numerals on the line below.

_____

**Name:** _____          **Date:** _____

15. Write eight thousandths in numerals on the line below.

   _____

16. Write ten and thirteen thousandths in numerals on the line below.

   _____

Name the following shaded areas as decimals and fractions:

17.
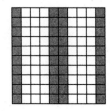

   _____

   _____

18.
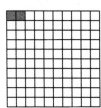

   _____

   _____

19.
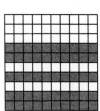

   _____

   _____

20.
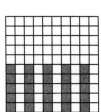

   _____

   _____

**Name:** _____     **Date:** _____

# Decimal Applications

Tanya's grade point average was 3.26 in her freshman year, 3.3 in her sophomore year, and 3.09 in her junior year.

1. In which year did she have her best grade point?_____

2. In which year did she have her worst grade point?_____

3. What is the largest number that can be constructed by ordering the digits 5, 9, and 2 and by placing a decimal point in the number?

   Write your answer on the line below.

   _____

4. What is the smallest number that can be constructed using the same digits as above and a decimal point?

   Write your answer on the line below.

   _____

5. Taxpayers in Urbanville paid 37.090 mills for school taxes.

   Which amount below is the same as 37.090?

       a. 37.9       b. 37.09       c. not given       d. I don't know.

**Name:** _____     **Date:** _____

6. One large spiral notebook costs $1.87. How much will four notebooks cost?
   *Set up the problem and solve.*

7. An enthusiastic runner wanted to jog 1000 miles in 1 year. She jogged 125.55 miles in
   January and 105.5 miles in February. How many miles did she run in these 2 months?
   *Set up the problem and solve.*

8. Using the answer from Problem #7, figure out how many more miles the runner needs
   to jog this year to reach her goal of 1000 miles. *Set up the problem and solve.*

**Name:** _____     **Date:** _____

# Tenths Review

My cat had ten kittens. Seven were black, and three were calico.

1. On the grid below, shade in the decimal fraction that represents the portion of the kittens that are black. Express the answer in three different ways.

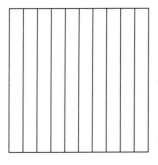

_____   _____   _____

2. On the grid below, shade in the decimal fraction which represents the portion of the kittens that are calico. Express the answer in three different ways.

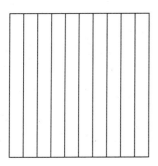

_____   _____   _____

3. Shade the grid below to show the entire litter of kittens my cat had. Write the shaded amount in three different ways.

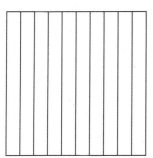

_____   _____   _____

# Counting Squares—Tenths

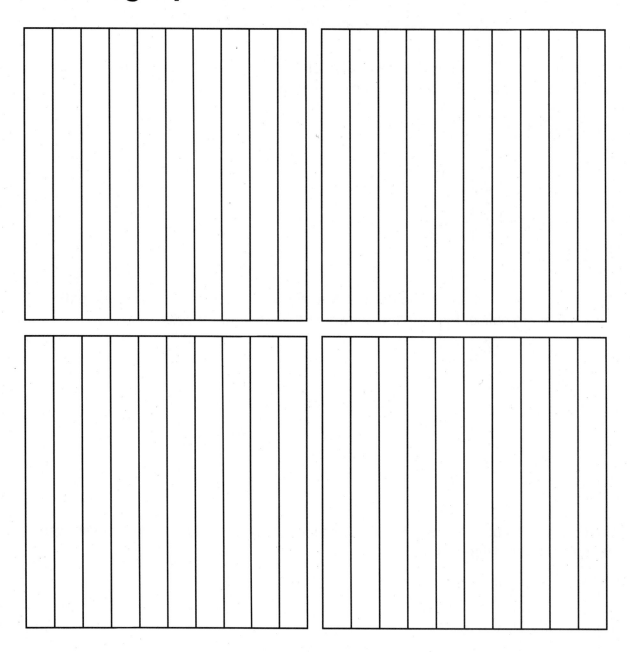

**Name:** _____    **Date:** _____

# Decimal Word Problems

Directions: Write the answer to each problem three ways: as a fraction (1/10), a decimal fraction (.1), and in words (one tenth).

1. Mr. Suburbia is re-sodding his lawn. The counting square is shaded to show the portion of the job that he has completed.

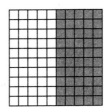

   a. What number represents the sodded area? Write it in three ways.

   _____    _____    _____

   b. What portion is not yet sodded?

   _____    _____    _____

2. The mythical kingdom of Cypher has designed a new flag.

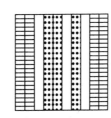

   a. What portion of the flag has horizontal stripes?

   _____    _____    _____

   b. What portion of the flag is dotted?

   _____    _____    _____

   c. What portion of the flag is plain?

   _____    _____    _____

**Name:** _____

**Date:** _____

3. Sheila's garden is magnificent. She has grown award-winning roses, daisies, and tulips. Four tenths of her garden is roses, and one half of her garden is daisies. The rest of her garden is tulips.

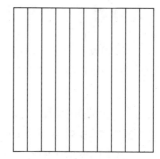

Shade the counting square to show how much of her garden is tulips and write it in three ways below:

_____     _____     _____

4. One of Brad's beach towels is black and white.

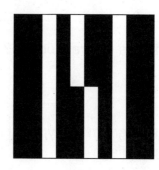

What portion of Brad's towel is black? Write it in three ways below:

_____     _____     _____

5. Mr. Greatwealth is building a new store. He will use three tenths of the store to sell groceries, one tenth of the store to sell housewares, and the rest of the store will be devoted to clothing.

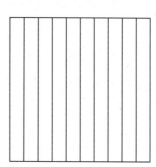

Shade the counting square to show how much of the store will be devoted to clothing and write it in three ways below:

_____     _____     _____

**Name:** _____     **Date:** _____

6.  One half of the space allotted for
    clothing in Mr. Greatwealth's store will
    be used for hats and shoes. What
    portion of the store is devoted to hats
    and shoes? Shade this amount on the
    counting square on the right.

7.  As you recall, Mr. Suburbia was
    resodding his entire lawn. He has just
    finished the job. The counting square
    on the right represents Mr. Suburbia's
    yard. Shade in the area to show his
    completed work.

    Write the answer in three ways.

    _____    _____    _____

8.  The pirate flag of Capt. Evil is half black
    and half red. Shade in the area to show
    how much is black on the counting
    square on the right.

    Write the answer in three ways.

    _____    _____    _____

**Name:** _____     **Date:** _____

9.  Four tenths of Sheila's garden is roses. Oh,
    dear! Aphids infested half of them. Shade in
    the portion of her garden that still has
    healthy roses.

    Write the portion that is shaded in three ways.

    _____     _____     _____

10. Autumn leaves are covering nine tenths
    (9/10) of Mr. Suburbia's yard and all of his
    neighbor's yard. Shade in the area to show
    how much is covered in leaves on the
    counting squares on the right.

    Write the shaded amount in three ways.

    _____     _____     _____

**Name:** _____          **Date:** _____

# Composing Decimal Problems

Directions: Write three story problems involving tenths in the spaces below. Shade the counting square next to the story problem to show the answer.

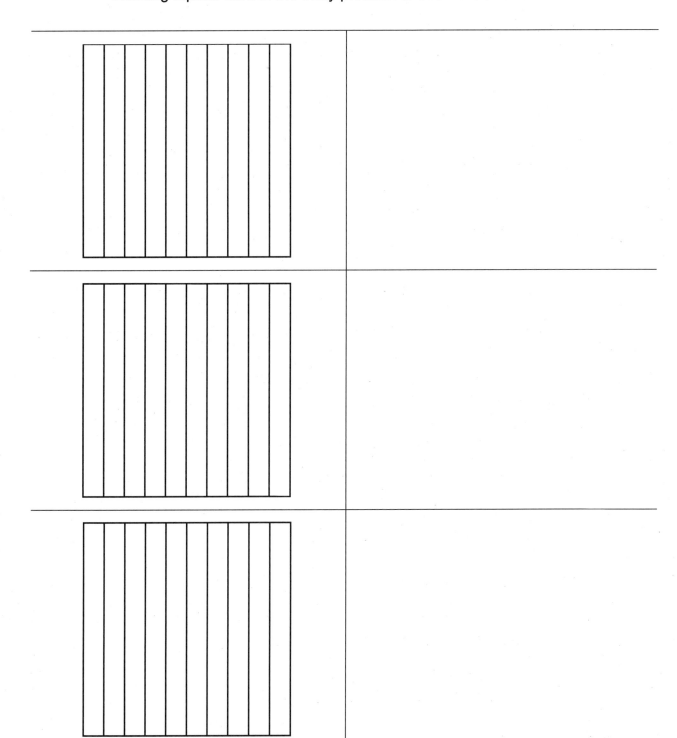

**Name:** _____

**Date:** _____

# Tenths and Mixed Numbers

1. Shade 1.3

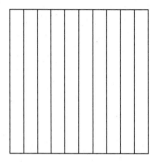

2. Identify the shaded area. Write it in three ways.

   _____

   _____

   _____

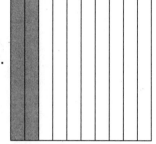

3. Identify the shaded area. Write it in three ways.

   _____

   _____

   _____

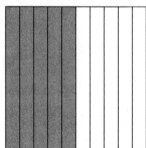

4. Shade 10 tenths.

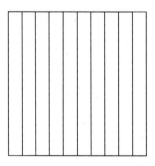

5. Identify the shaded area. Write it in three ways.

   _____

   _____

   _____

 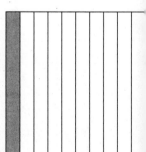

**Name:** _____      **Date:** _____

# Ordering Decimals

1. Order from smallest to largest:

   319.8          _____

   309.6          _____

   390.87         _____

   309.56         _____

   309.78         _____

   309.07         _____


2. Order from largest to smallest:

   .58            _____

   .8             _____

   .85            _____

   .55            _____

   .57            _____

   .08            _____

# High Decimal Rummy

| | | |
|:---:|:---:|:---:|
| 0.4 | 0.36 | 0.43 |
| 0.68 | 0.62 | 0.34 |
| 0.86 | 0.8 | 0.08 |
| 0.04 | 0.26 | 0.5 |
| 0.84 | 0.7 | 0.53 |

# Counting Squares—Tenths and Hundredths

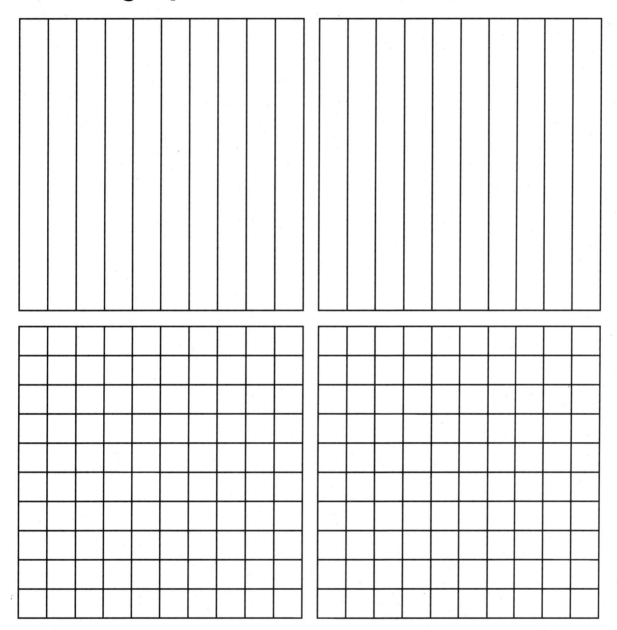

# Tenths Overlay

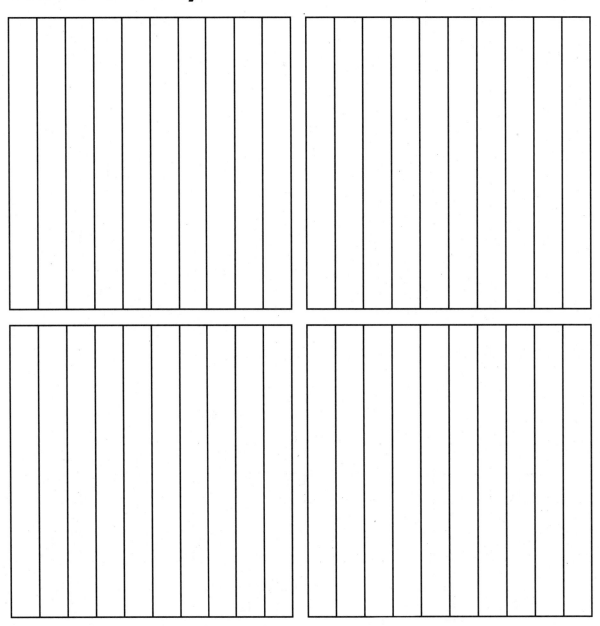

**Name:** _____

**Date:** _____

# Sixteen Counting Squares

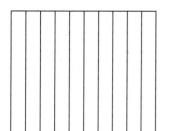
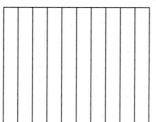
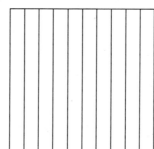
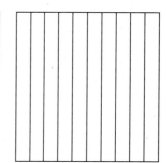
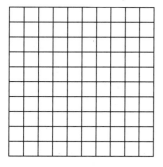
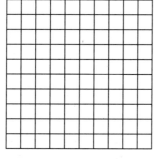
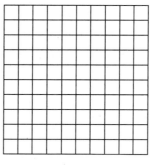
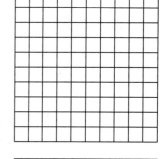
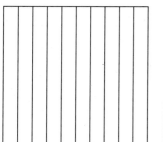
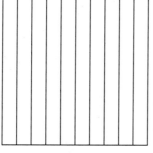
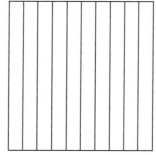
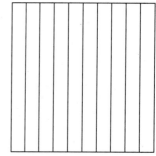
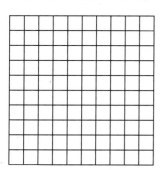
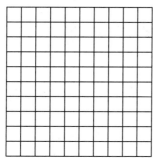

**Name:** _____     **Date:** _____

# Shading and Naming Equivalences

1. Shade .7

Shade the equivalent area.
in hundredths.

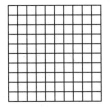

2. Name the shaded area.

_____

Shade the equivalent area.

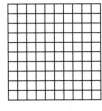

3. Shade .10

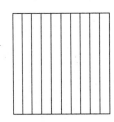

Shade the equivalent area.

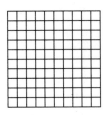

4. Name the shaded area.

_____

Shade the equivalent area.

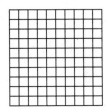

5. Shade 10/10

Shade the equivalent area.

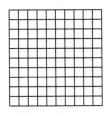

6. Name the shaded area.

_____

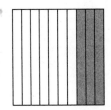

Shade the equivalent area.

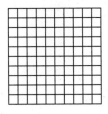

     

**Name:** _____    **Date:** _____

# Tenths and Hundredths Review

1. Shade the equivalent of .6

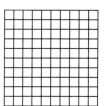

2. Shade .30

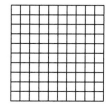

3. Shade .03

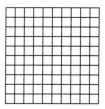

4. Circle the one that is larger:

   .28      .3

5. What number is shaded?
   Write it in two ways.

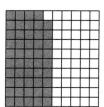

6. What number is shaded?
   Write it in three ways.

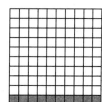

**Name:** _____     **Date:** _____

# Decimal Fractions

Ms. Hane made a cake with a 100 pieces. The class ate six tenths of them.

1.  Write a decimal that shows how many pieces were left. _____

2.  Write that amount in another way. _____

3.  If .75 of the cake had been eaten, then how much of the cake would be left? Write a decimal to show that amount.

    _____

Michael bought a game that has 100 marbles.

    30 of the marbles are green.

    20 of the marbles are white.

    40 of the marbles are red.

    10 of the marbles are blue.

4.  Write the decimal that tells what portion of the marbles are green. _____

5.  What portion of the marbles are colors other than white? Write the answer in two ways.

    _____     _____

6.  Forty of the 100 marbles are red. How many tenths of the marbles are red?

    _____

**Name:** _____     **Date:** _____

7. Write these numbers in order from smallest to largest.

| .50 | .10 | .235 | 1.0 | .9 |

____     ____     ____     ____     ____

Look at the two numbers in each line.

Circle (Yes) if they are equivalent.

Circle (No) if they are not equivalent.

| | | | | |
|-----|----------|-------------|-----|----|
| 8. | .10 | .1 | Yes | No |
| 9. | .040 | .04 | Yes | No |
| 10. | 1 ten | 1 tenth | Yes | No |
| 11. | .50 | .05 | Yes | No |
| 12. | 1 tenth | .01 | Yes | No |
| 13. | .40 | 40/100 | Yes | No |
| 14. | .300 | .3 | Yes | No |
| 15. | .008 | .080 | Yes | No |
| 16. | 6/10 | .60 | Yes | No |
| 17. | .01 | 1 hundredth | Yes | No |

Add 3 tenths and 6 hundredths.

18. Write the number. _____

19. Write a decimal to show the value of the tenths. _____

20. Add 4 hundredths to the number. Write a decimal to show the answer.

_____

# Counting Squares—Hundredths

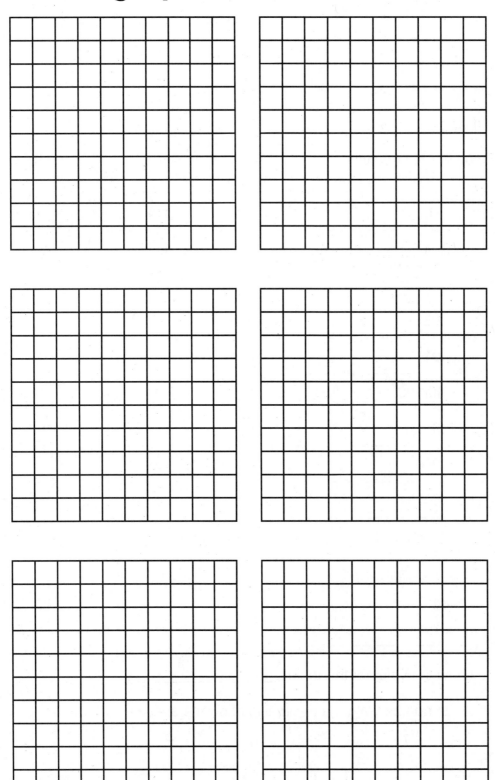

   

**Name:** _____

**Date:** _____

# Subtraction Story Problems

1. Janet's cat, Musk, weighs 3.5 lbs. Linda's cat, Tabby, weighs 3.42 lbs.

   a. Shade the grids to show how much each cat weighed.

MUSK

TABBY

   b. Which cat weighs more?_____

   c. How much more?_____

   d. Set up the problem and solve. Show your work below:

**Name:** _____      **Date:** _____

2.   Marcia bought 1 pound of candy. She ate the shaded amount.

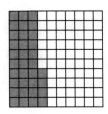

     a.   How much candy did she eat?_____

     b.   How much did she have left?_____

     c.   Set up the problem and solve. Show your work below:

3.   Dad bought 2.4 gallons of gas and filled his lawn mower with 1.75 gallons.

     a.   How much is left in the gas can?_____

     b.   Set up the problem and solve. Show your work below:

                

**Name:** _____　　　**Date:** _____

# Ordering and Computing Prices and Weights

Note: Unit Price is the price per pound.

| Chocolate Drops | | |
|---|---|---|
| Net Weight | Unit Price | Total |
| 0.79 lb | $1.89 | $1.49 |

| Lollypops | | |
|---|---|---|
| Net Weight | Unit Price | Total |
| 1.19 lb | $1.59 | $1.89 |

| Butterscotch Discs | | |
|---|---|---|
| Net Weight | Unit Price | Total |
| 1.10 lb | $1.19 | $1.31 |

| Cherry Candy | | |
|---|---|---|
| Net Weight | Unit Price | Total |
| 0.50 lb | $1.89 | $0.95 |

| Jelly Beans | | |
|---|---|---|
| Net Weight | Unit Price | Total |
| 0.91 lb | $1.59 | $1.45 |

1. Order the totals from least to greatest.

   _____　　_____　　_____　　_____　　_____

2. Order the net weights from lightest to heaviest.

   _____　　_____　　_____　　_____　　_____

3. What is the total cost of *all* the candy?_____
   Show your work.

4. What is the total weight of *all* the candy?_____
   Show your work.

**Name:** _____     **Date:** _____

5.  What would 3 pounds of Jelly Beans cost?_____
    Show your work.

6.  How much would you have to pay for one half of a pound of Jelly

    Beans?_____
    Show your work.

7.  Name two different items you could buy if you had $2.50._____
    Show your work.

8.  What would 5 pounds of Lollypops cost?_____
    Show your work.

9.  What is the difference in weight between the Lollypops and the Chocolate Drops?

    _____
    Show your work.

10. What would 2 pounds of Chocolate Drops and 2 pounds of Butterscotch Discs cost

    combined?_____
    Show your work.

**Name:** _____          **Date:** _____

# Comparing and Computing Distances

A group of students rode their bikes to Keeny Middle School yesterday.

David rode 3.41 miles.

Lisa rode 3.95 miles.

Steve rode 3.50 miles.

Susie rode 3.8 miles.

Todd rode 4 miles.

1. Who rode the farthest? _____

2. Who had the shortest ride? _____

3. How many miles did Steve and Susie ride in all? _____

4. If Lisa rode her bike to school and then back home, how many miles did she ride?

   _____

5. How many more miles did Todd ride than David? _____

6. How many miles did the girls ride together? _____

7. What is the total number of miles the students rode yesterday (assuming they all made a round trip to school and back home)?

   _____

**Name:** _____     **Date:** _____

# Tenths, Hundredths, Thousandths Review

1. Name the shaded area in two ways.

     _____

_____

2. Shade in the equivalent of .6, then write the number in hundredths and thousandths.

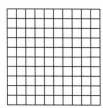     _____

_____

3. Name this number in two ways.

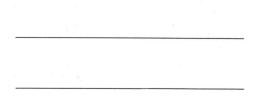

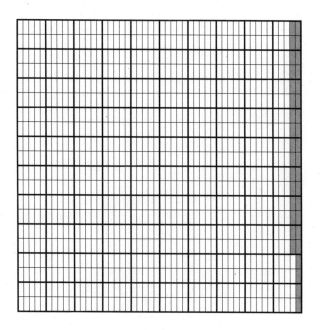

**Name:** _____        **Date:** _____

4.   Name this number in two ways.

_____

_____

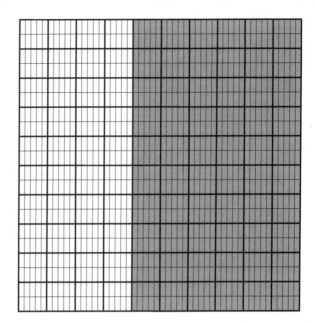

5.   Add together the three numbers represented by the shaded counting squares.
     Record the total.

_____ Show your work below.

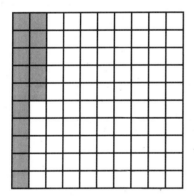   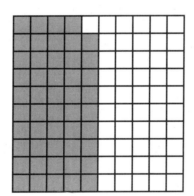   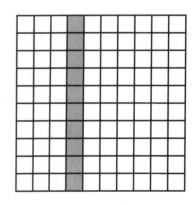

**Name:** _____      **Date:** _____

6.  What is the difference between .4 and .27? Write your answer. _____
    Show your work below.

7.  You ate .750 of a pizza. Show how much was eaten by shading the counting
    square below.

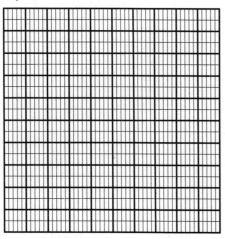

8.  How much of the pizza was not eaten? Write your answer.

    _____

9.  Add the following numbers: 5 tenths, 5 hundredths, 5 thousandths. Shade the counting
    square to show the total.

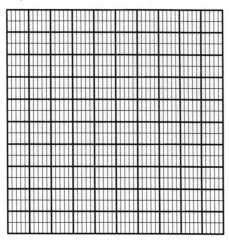

10. Fill in the blanks to complete this chart:

    10 _____          equals 1 hundredth

    10 hundredths                                 equals 1 _____

    10 _____          equals 1 whole

    10 ones                                       equals 1 _____

# Place Value Cards

| millions | ones | thousands | hundreds | ten thousands | hundredths |
|---|---|---|---|---|---|
| millions | thousandths | tens | hundred thousands | tenths | ● |
| millions | ones | thousands | hundreds | ten thousands | hundredths |
| thousandths | tens | hundred thousands | tenths | ● | |

BLACKLINE MASTERS   **191**

# Large Counting Square—Thousandths

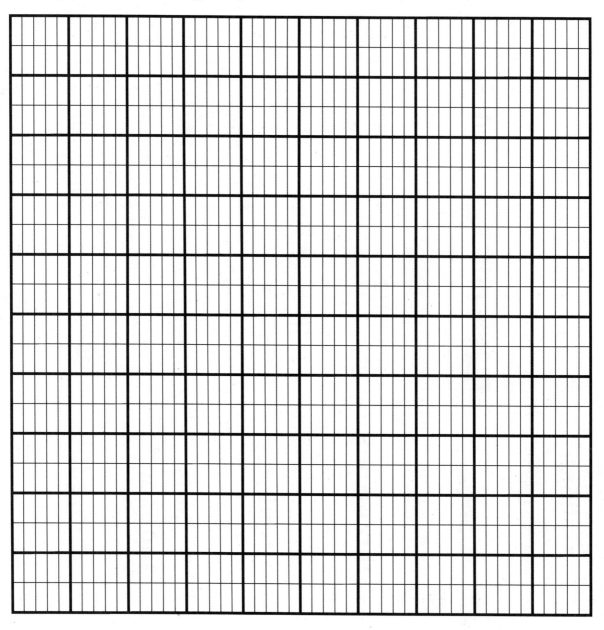

**Name:** _____          **Date:** _____

# Counting Squares—Thousandths

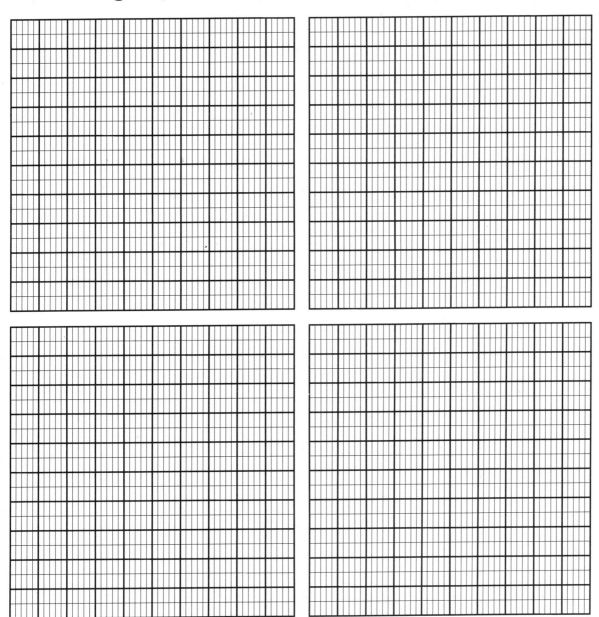

Name: _____     Date: _____

# Counting Squares—Tenths, Hundredths, Thousandths

1.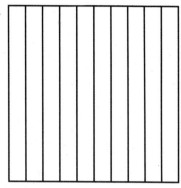

_____

2.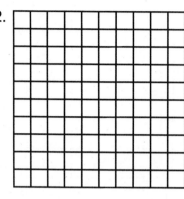

_____

3.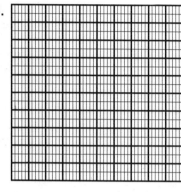

_____

4.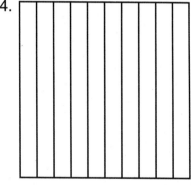

_____

5.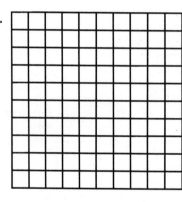

_____

6.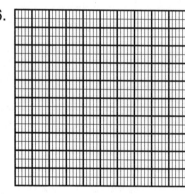

_____

7.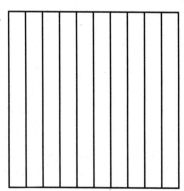

_____

8.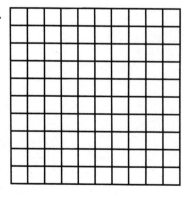

_____

9.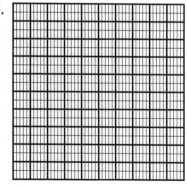

_____

# Decimal Patterns Ledger

| ten thousands | thousands | hundreds | tens | ones | tenths | hundredths | thousandths | ten thousandths |
|---|---|---|---|---|---|---|---|---|
| | | | | | | | | |
| | | | | | | | | |
| | | | | | | | | |
| | | | | | | | | |
| | | | | | | | | |
| | | | | | | | | |
| | | | | | | | | |
| | | | | | | | | |
| | | | | | | | | |
| | | | | | | | | |
| | | | | | | | | |
| | | | | | | | | |
| | | | | | | | | |
| | | | | | | | | |
| | | | | | | | | |
| | | | | | | | | |
| | | | | | | | | |

# Decimal Dough Coins

| | | | | | | | | | |
|---|---|---|---|---|---|---|---|---|---|
| dime .1 | dime .1 | dime .1 | dime .1 | dime .1 | dime .1 | dime .1 | dime .1 | dime .1 | dime .1 |
| dime .1 | dime .1 | dime .1 | dime .1 | dime .1 | dime .1 | dime .1 | dime .1 | dime .1 | dime .1 |
| dime .1 | dime .1 | dime .1 | dime .1 | dime .1 | dime .1 | dime .1 | dime .1 | dime .1 | dime .1 |
| dime .1 | dime .1 | dime .1 | dime .1 | dime .1 | dime .1 | dime .1 | dime .1 | dime .1 | dime .1 |
| dime .1 | dime .1 | dime .1 | dime .1 | dime .1 | dime .1 | dime .1 | dime .1 | dime .1 | dime .1 |
| dime .1 | dime .1 | dime .1 | dime .1 | dime .1 | dime .1 | dime .1 | dime .1 | dime .1 | dime .1 |
| dime .1 | dime .1 | dime .1 | dime .1 | dime .1 | dime .1 | dime .1 | dime .1 | dime .1 | dime .1 |

# Decimal Dough Coins

| | | | | | | | | | |
|---|---|---|---|---|---|---|---|---|---|
| penny .01 | penny .01 | penny .01 | penny .01 | penny .01 | penny .01 | penny .01 | penny .01 | penny .01 | penny .01 |
| penny .01 | penny .01 | penny .01 | penny .01 | penny .01 | penny .01 | penny .01 | penny .01 | penny .01 | penny .01 |
| penny .01 | penny .01 | penny .01 | penny .01 | penny .01 | penny .01 | penny .01 | penny .01 | penny .01 | penny .01 |
| penny .01 | penny .01 | penny .01 | penny .01 | penny .01 | penny .01 | penny .01 | penny .01 | penny .01 | penny .01 |
| penny .01 | penny .01 | penny .01 | penny .01 | penny .01 | penny .01 | penny .01 | penny .01 | penny .01 | penny .01 |
| penny .01 | penny .01 | penny .01 | penny .01 | penny .01 | penny .01 | penny .01 | penny .01 | penny .01 | penny .01 |
| penny .01 | penny .01 | penny .01 | penny .01 | penny .01 | penny .01 | penny .01 | penny .01 | penny .01 | penny .01 |

# Decimal Dough Coins

| | | | | | | | | | |
|---|---|---|---|---|---|---|---|---|---|
| mill .001 | mill .001 | mill .001 | mill .001 | mill .001 | mill .001 | mill .001 | mill .001 | mill .001 | mill .001 |
| mill .001 | mill .001 | mill .001 | mill .001 | mill .001 | mill .001 | mill .001 | mill .001 | mill .001 | mill .001 |
| mill .001 | mill .001 | mill .001 | mill .001 | mill .001 | mill .001 | mill .001 | mill .001 | mill .001 | mill .001 |
| mill .001 | mill .001 | mill .001 | mill .001 | mill .001 | mill .001 | mill .001 | mill .001 | mill .001 | mill .001 |
| mill .001 | mill .001 | mill .001 | mill .001 | mill .001 | mill .001 | mill .001 | mill .001 | mill .001 | mill .001 |
| mill .001 | mill .001 | mill .001 | mill .001 | mill .001 | mill .001 | mill .001 | mill .001 | mill .001 | mill .001 |
| mill .001 | mill .001 | mill .001 | mill .001 | mill .001 | mill .001 | mill .001 | mill .001 | mill .001 | mill .001 |

**Name:** _____

**Date:** _____

# Adding Thousandths

| | |
|---|---|
| 1<br><br>.450<br>+.005 | 2<br><br>.455<br>+.005 |

| | | | |
|---|---|---|---|
| 3 | 4 | | |

| | | | |
|---|---|---|---|
| 5 | 6 | 7 | 8 |

| | | | |
|---|---|---|---|
| 9 | 10 | 11 | 12 |

| | | | |
|---|---|---|---|
| 13 | 14 | 15 | 16 |

| | | | |
|---|---|---|---|
| 17 | 18 | 19 | 20 |

# Decimal Dough Coins for Overhead

| | | | | | |
|---|---|---|---|---|---|
| dime .1 | dime .1 | penny .01 | penny .01 | mill .001 | mill .001 |
| dime .1 | dime .1 | penny .01 | penny .01 | mill .001 | mill .001 |
| dime .1 | dime .1 | penny .01 | penny .01 | mill .001 | mill .001 |
| dime .1 | dime .1 | penny .01 | penny .01 | mill .001 | mill .001 |
| dime .1 | dime .1 | penny .01 | penny .01 | mill .001 | mill .001 |
| dime .1 | dime .1 | penny .01 | penny .01 | mill .001 | mill .001 |
| dime .1 | dime .1 | penny .01 | penny .01 | mill .001 | mill .001 |
| dime .1 | dime .1 | penny .01 | penny .01 | mill .001 | mill .001 |
| dime .1 | dime .1 | penny .01 | penny .01 | mill .001 | mill .001 |
| dime .1 | dime .1 | penny .01 | penny .01 | mill .001 | mill .001 |

**Name:** _____

**Date:** _____

# Subtracting Thousandths

| | | | |
|---|---|---|---|
| 1<br><br>  .500<br>− .009 | 2<br><br>  .491<br>− .009 | 3 | 4 |
| 5 | 6 | 7 | 8 |
| 9 | 10 | 11 | 12 |
| 13 | 14 | 15 | 16 |
| 17 | 18 | 19 | 20 |

**Name:** _____

**Date:** _____

# Sports Problems

## Batting Averages

| Name | Batting Average |
|------|-----------------|
| Casey | .235 |
| Babe | .335 |
| Ty | .347 |
| Slim | .298 |
| Slugger | .267 |
| Stretch | .280 |
| Joe | .198 |
| Jake | .253 |

## Men's Weight Lifting

| Name | Pounds Lifted |
|------|---------------|
| Bruno | 1151.57 |
| Max | 1139.21 |
| Hercules | 1130.43 |
| Ivan | 1157.41 |
| Thor | 1127.65 |
| Edwin | 1119.76 |
| Percy | 1128.99 |
| Steve | 1140.88 |

## Women's 100-Meter Backstroke

| Name | Time in Seconds | |
|------|-----------------|-----------------|
| | Time Trial #1 | Time Trial #2 |
| Esther | 56.702 | 57.251 |
| Donna | 56.793 | 56.659 |
| Ariel | 55.990 | 57.024 |
| Coral | 59.026 | 55.999 |
| Marilyn | 58.729 | 55.978 |
| Pearl | 57.025 | 57.427 |
| Lydia | 54.995 | 58.046 |
| June | 54.995 | 55.683 |

## Women's 400-Meter Run

| Name | Time in Seconds | |
|------|-----------------|-----------------|
| | Time Trial #1 | Time Trial #2 |
| Alison | 49.032 | 48.872 |
| Michelle | 59.014 | 49.231 |
| Peg | 48.831 | 49.369 |
| Aurora | 50.973 | 48.101 |
| Lisa | 47.992 | 48.722 |
| Samantha | 49.496 | 51.371 |
| Stacy | 48.171 | 48.114 |
| Robin | 49.732 | 50.011 |

**Name:** _____    **Date:** _____

# Sports Problems

1. Order the number of pounds lifted by each man from the greatest to the least.

   Name                                    Weight

   _____        _____

   _____        _____

   _____        _____

   _____        _____

   _____        _____

   _____        _____

2. Who improved their time in the Women's 100-Meter Backstroke during their second trial?

   _____

   _____

   _____

3. Which of the three improved their time the most? _____
   To prove your answer, show your work below.

4. What was the difference in time between the fastest and slowest swimmer in Time Trial #2? Show your work below.

   _____

5. The winner of the first trial of the 400-Meter Run was Lisa with a time of 47.992 seconds. Who is the winner of the second trial?

   _____

6. Was her time better than Lisa's time of 47.992? _____

7. How much faster was Lisa's time in the first trial than Aurora's in the second trial? Show your work below.

   _____

8. A luxury sedan weighs 4623 pounds. Would Ivan, Steve, Max, and Thor together be able to lift it? Show your work below.

   _____

9. How much more did the winner of the Men's Weight Lifting Contest lift than the second place finisher? Show your work below.

   _____

10. Order the players with the five highest batting averages.

    | Name | Batting Average |
    |------|-----------------|
    | _____ | _____ |
    | _____ | _____ |
    | _____ | _____ |
    | _____ | _____ |
    | _____ | _____ |

**Name:** _____          **Date:** _____

# Counting Squares for Mixed Numbers

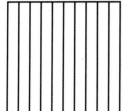 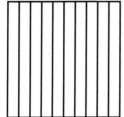 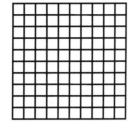 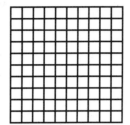 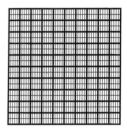

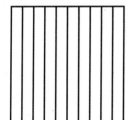 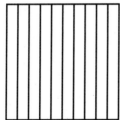 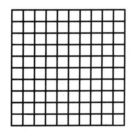 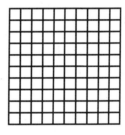 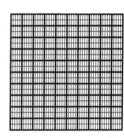

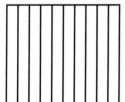 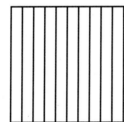 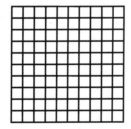 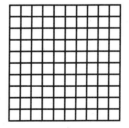 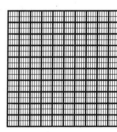

# Robo-Batter

Use the data from page 1 of *Worksheet 10C: Sports Problems* to solve these problems.

1.  Combine the batting averages of three players to find the closest possible number to a perfect 1.000 (or 1000 hits for 1000 times at bat).

    | Player | Batting Average |
    | --- | --- |
    | _____ | _____ |
    | _____ | _____ |
    | _____ | _____ |

    Total:

2.  Find the difference between the highest and lowest batting average.

    | Player | Batting Average |
    | --- | --- |
    | _____ | _____ |
    | _____ | _____ |

    Difference:

3.  Stretch hopes to bat .500 by the season's end. How many more hits per 1000 must Stretch get to achieve his goal? Set up the problem and solve.

    _____

4.  Last season Babe's batting average was .239. By what decimal fraction has his batting average improved? Set up the problem and solve.

    _____

5.  If Jake's batting average were to double, what would be his new batting average? Set up the problem and solve.

    _____

# Decimal Dough Story Problems

1. Ms. Schaefer has counted all of the money in her purse. She has counted a total of 6 ones, 8 tenths, 5 hundredths, and 7 mills.

   Display the amount of money that Ms. Schaefer has on the place value chart using your Decimal Dough. Then answer the following questions:

   a. How much Decimal Dough does she have?        _____

   b. How many dimes does she have?        _____

   c. How many pennies does she have?        _____

   d. If she were to trade in two of her dollars for dimes, how many dimes would she get?        _____

2. Mrs. Thomas has counted all of the money in her purse. She counted a total of 9 ten-dollar bills, 6 dollars, 8 dimes, and 4 pennies.

   Display the amount of money that Mrs. Thomas has on the place value chart using your Decimal Dough. Then answer the following questions:

   a. How much money does she have?        _____

   b. Write a decimal for the value of the dimes she has.        _____

   c. Write a decimal for the value of the pennies she has.        _____

   d. How many hundredths does she have counting both dimes and pennies?        _____

   e. How much more does she need to have a total of $100.00?        _____

**Name:** _____     **Date:** _____

# Checkbook Problems

1. Your grandmother sends a birthday card. Inside the card you find $150.00. Have a good time!

2. Your brother helps you with your chores so you can meet your friends and go to a movie. You pay him $10.451.

3. You decide to sell your motor bike to your best friend for $204.071. Your account grows.

4. Oops! You just put a baseball through your neighbor's window. Unfortunately, it was a double pane window and it costs $158.950. Look out slugger!

5. To encourage savings, your great aunt has offered to match the funds in any of her nieces' or nephews' bank accounts. Since you are one of the lucky few who has money in the bank, her gift doubles your bank balance. Super saver!

6. Your friend's family is taking you on vacation with them. Before you leave, you have to chip in for gas, food, and lodging. That comes to $43.50. Happy traveling!

7. You bought a can of soda pop every day for a week. It was $.65 a can, and it's time to pay your week's bill. Was it a thirst quencher?

8. It's payday. Your math teacher called your mom today with good news! Your mom decides to add a bonus to your allowance. She hands you $12.50! Put it in your account. What is your final balance?

Start with a $0.00 balance. Each transaction is listed in the first column. Compute your balance in the second column. Finally, record your balance in the third column.

| Description | Computation | Balance |
| --- | --- | --- |
| No money | | $0.00 |
| 1. Grandmother gives money | | |
| 2. Pay brother to help with chores | | |
| 3. Sell motorbike | | |
| 4. Broke a window | | |
| 5. Aunt doubles your balance | | |
| 6. Chip in for gas, food, lodging | | |
| 7. Bill for soda pop | | |
| 8. Mom gives a bonus | | |

**Name:** _____                **Date:** _____

# Kingdom of Wize Problems

| County | Annual Snowfall | Average Family Income | Area in Square Miles |
|--------|-----------------|-----------------------|----------------------|
| Clever | 50.363 inches | $9,456,111.07 | 1099.017 square miles |
| Shrewd | 45.452 inches | $9,564,002.11 | 1100.195 square miles |
| Wiley | 55.009 inches | $8,999,498.99 | 99.891 square miles |

1  a. Which county is the largest? _____

   b. Which county is the smallest? _____

   c. What is the difference in square miles between these 2 counties? Show your

      work below. _____

2. The three counties in the Kingdom of Wize cover a total of _____ square
   miles. Show your work below.

3. Clever and Shrewd cover about the same area in square miles. What is the difference
   in square miles between these 2 counties? Show your work below.

   _____

4. Which county is the richest ? _____

5. How much more is the average family income of Shrewd than the average family

   income of Wiley? Show your work below. _____

6. Clever gets less snowfall than Wiley. How much less snow does Clever get, on

   average, each winter. Show your work below. _____

# ANSWER KEY

## Assessment IA: Whole Numbers

| | | | | | |
|---|---|---|---|---|---|
| 1. | b | 2. | a | 3. | d |
| 4. | d | 5. | b | 6. | 927 |
| 7. | 2,348 | 8. | 8,016 | 9. | 5,012 |
| 10. | 360 | 11. | 67 | 12. | 4,510 |
| 13. | 3,007 | 14. | 29 | 15. | 102 |

## Assessment IB: Whole Numbers Applications

| | | | |
|---|---|---|---|
| 1. | 1,219 stamps | 2. | 29 stamps |
| 3. | $300. | 4. | $8,385. |
| 5a. | $10. | 5b. | $50. |
| 5c. | $100. | 6. | $900. |

## Worksheet IA: Show Your Age

Answers will vary.

## Worksheet IB: Value of Digits

| | | | |
|---|---|---|---|
| 1. | 9 thousand | 2. | 7530 |
| 3. | 999 | 4. | 99 |
| 5. | 0 hundreds | 6. | 8,765 |
| 7. | 1,259 | | |

**UNIT TWO**

## Worksheet 2A: Catalogue Shopping

| | | | |
|---|---|---|---|
| 1. | $222. | 2. | $404. |
| 3. | $535. | 4. | $ 80. |
| 5. | No | | |

## Worksheet 2B: Flexible Regrouping

1a. Yes              1b. $130.

2. 22 tens and 6 ones (answers may vary: e.g., 20 tens, 26 ones)

3. 226 ones       4. 2 hundreds

5. 2 tens and 6 ones, or 1 ten and 16 ones

## Worksheet 2C: Numbers Out of Sequence

| | | | | | |
|---|---|---|---|---|---|
| 1. | 25 | 2. | 236 | 3. | 199 |
| 4. | 181 | 5. | 40 | 6. | 112 |
| 7. | 222 | 8. | 240 | 9. | 236 |
| 10. | 99 lb | 11. | 1 lb | | |

## UNIT THREE

## Worksheet 3A: Addition Recording Sheet

0, 5, 10, 15, ..., 110, 115, 120

## Worksheet 3B: Patterns of Five Ledger

0     000

5     005

0     010

etc.

## Worksheet 3C: Subtraction Recording Sheet

119, 118, 117, 116, ..., 105

100, 95, 90, ... , 60, 55, 50

## Worksheet 3D: Addition and Subtraction Recording Sheet

47, 54, 62, 39, 69, 100, 89, 111,........

## Worksheet 3E: Shopping List Problems

1. $90.
2. $953.
3. 13 items
4. 3 games, $19. left over
5. $37.
6. $99.
7. Perfume, blouse, training shoes, flowers, nail polish = $119.
8. Skateboard, bike, in-line skates, airplane ticket = $1126. or $1,199. with cross-training shoes.

## UNIT FOUR

### Worksheet 4A: Hundreds Ledger

70, 67, 60, 45, 26
182, 121, 82, 7, 1

### Worksheet 4B: Thousands Ledger

912, 813, 714, 615, 516, 417
1910, 1821, 1732, 1643, 1554, 1465

## UNIT FIVE

### Assessment 5A: Flexible Regrouping

1. ten
2. thousand
3. hundred
4. 5 thousands, 6 hundreds, 4 tens, 2 ones,
   or 56 hundreds, 4 tens, 2 ones
   or 564 tens, 2 ones
   or 5,642 ones
5. 6 thousands, 0 hundreds, 0 tens, 2 ones
   or 60 hundreds, 0 tens, 2 ones
   or 600 tens, 2 ones
   or 6,002 ones
6. Answers may vary. (e.g., the 4 thousands in 4,294 can be regrouped into 40 hundreds, plus the 2 hundreds in the hundreds place = 42 hundreds, 9 tens, and 4 ones.)

## UNIT SIX

### Assessment 6A: Decimal Concepts

1. c                    2. .33                3. Shade 7 tenths (.7).
4. Shade 7 hundredths (.07).        5. Shade 75 hundredths (.75).
6. Shading will be approximate; should be a little more than half.
7. a          8. d          9. c
10. d          11. b          12. a
13. 0.57, .57      14. 0.4, .4        15. 0.008, .008
16. 10.013        17. 0.4, 4/10, 0.40, 40/100
18. 0.02, 2/100    19. 0.5, 5/10, 0.50, 50/100, 1/2, etc.
20. 0.25, 25/100, 1/4

## Assessment 6B: Decimal Applications

1. 3.3 (sophomore year)
2. 3.09 (junior year)
3. 95.2 or 952.0
4. .259
5. b
6. $7.48
7. 231.05 miles
8. 768.95 miles

## Assessment 6C: Tenths Review

1. Shade .7; write .7, 7/10, seven tenths.
2. Shade .3; write .3, 3/10, three tenths.
3. Shade 1.0; write 1.0, 10/10, 100/100, one and zero tenths.

## Worksheet 6A: Decimal Word Problems

1a. .5, five tenths, 5/10, 1/2
1b. .5, five tenths, 5/10, 1/2
2a. .4, four tenths, 4/10
2b. .3, three tenths, 3/10
2c. .3, three tenths, 3/10
3. tulips = .1, 1/10, one tenth
4. black = .7, 7/10, seven tenths
5. clothing = .6, 6/10, six tenths
6. hats and shoes = .3, 3/10, three tenths
7. Shade 10/10 or the entire grid
8. Shade 5/10: write .5, 5/10, 1/2, five tenths
9. Shade 2/10: write .2, 2/10, two tenths
10. Shade 1.9: write 1.9, 1 9/10, one and nine tenths

## Worksheet 6B: Composing Decimal Problems

Answers will vary.

## UNIT SEVEN

## Assessment 7A: Tenths and Mixed Numbers

1. Shade 1 and 3/10
2. .2, 2/10, two tenths
3. .5, 5/10, five tenths
4. Shade one whole grid (10/10)
5. 1.1, 1 1/10, one and one tenth

## Assessment 7B: Ordering Decimals

1.  309.07        309.56        309.6
    309.78        319.8         390.87

2.  .85           .8            .58
    .57           .55           .08

## Worksheet 7B: Shading and Naming Equivalences

1.  Shade 7 tenths, 70 hundredths.
2.  .5, shade 50 hundredths
3.  Shade 1 tenth, then shade 10 hundredths.
4.  .9, shade 90 hundredths.
5.  Shade 1 whole, then shade 100 hundredths.
6.  0.3, shade 30 hundredths.

## UNIT EIGHT

## Assessment 8A: Tenths and Hundredths Review

1.  Shade 60 hundredths.          2.  Shade 30 hundredths.
3.  Shade 3 hundredths.           4.  .3
5.  49/100, .49, forty-nine hundredths     6.  .1, .10, ten hundredths

## Assessment 8B: Decimal Fractions

1.  .40 or .4        2.  .4 or .40, 4/10, 40/100, or 40 pieces
3.  .25              4.  .30, or .3
5.  .80, .8. 80/100, 8/10, etc.
6.  4 tenths, .4, four tenths, 4/10
7.  .10, .235, .50, .9, 1.0
8.  Yes         9.  Yes         10.  No
11. No          12. No          13.  Yes
14. Yes         15. No          16.  Yes
17. Yes         18. .36         19.  .3
20. .40 or .4

## Worksheet 8A: Subtraction Story Problems with Grids

1a. Shade 3 wholes and 5 tenths for Musk.
    Shade 3 wholes and 42 hundredths for Tabby.
1b. Musk
1c. .08 of a pound
1d.   3.5
    − 3.42
      .08
2a. 34 hundredths of a pound of candy

2b. 66 hundredths of a pound of candy

2c.   1.00
     − .34
      .66

3a. .65 gallon of gas

3b.   2.4
     − 1.75
      .65

## Worksheet 8B: Ordering and Computing Prices and Weights

1. $.95, $1.31, $1.45, $1.49, $1.89
2. .50 lb, .79 lb, .91 lb, 1.10 lb, 1.19 lb
3. $7.09
4. 4.49 lb
5. $4.77
6. $.80
7. Chocolate drops and cherry candy, or butterscotch discs and cherry candy, or cherry candy and jelly beans, or two packages of cherry candy
8. $7.95
9. .40 lb, .4 lb, or 4/10 lb
10. $6.16

## Worksheet 8C: Comparing and Computing Distances

1. Todd, (4 miles)   2.   David, (3.41 miles)
3. 7.3 miles          4.   7.9 miles
5. .59 miles or 59/100 of a mile
6. 7.75 miles         7.   37.32 miles

**UNIT NINE**

## Assessment 9A: Tenths, Hundredths, Thousandths Review

1. .4, .40, .400, 4/10, 40/100, 400/1,000, four tenths, etc.
2. Shade 60 hundredths; write .60, .600, 60/100, 600/1,000, 60 hundredths, 600 thousandths.
3. .036, 36 thousandths
4. .600, .60, .6, 600/1,000, 60/100, 6/10, 600 thousandths, 60 hundredths, 6 tenths
5. .74
6. .13
7. Shade 750 thousandths.
8. .250, .25
9. Shade 555 thousandths.
10. thousandths, tenth, tenths, ten

## Worksheet 10A: Adding Thousandths

.455, .460, .465, .470, ..., .545, .550

## Worksheet 10B: Subtracting Thousandths

.491, .482, .473, .464, .455, .446, .437, .428, .419, .410, .401, .392, .383, .374, .365, .356, .347, .338, .329, .320

## Worksheet 10C: Sports Problems

1.  | Ivan     | 1,157.41 |
    | Bruno    | 1,151.57 |
    | Steve    | 1,140.88 |
    | Max      | 1,139.21 |
    | Hercules | 1,130.43 |
    | Percy    | 1,128.99 |
    | Thor     | 1,127.65 |
    | Edwin    | 1,119.76 |

2.  Donna, Coral, Marilyn

3.  Coral
$$\begin{array}{r} 59.026 \\ -55.999 \\ \hline 3.027 \text{ seconds} \end{array}$$

4.  2.363 seconds

5.  Aurora

6.  No

7.  .109 seconds

8.  No
$$\begin{array}{r} 1,157.41 \\ 1,140.88 \\ 1,139.21 \\ +1,127.65 \\ \hline 4,565.15 \text{ pounds} \end{array}$$

9.  5.84 pounds
$$\begin{array}{r} 1,157.41 \\ -1,151.57 \\ \hline 5.84 \text{ pounds} \end{array}$$

10. | Ty      | .347 |
    | Babe    | .335 |
    | Slim    | .298 |
    | Stretch | .280 |
    | Slugger | .267 |

## Worksheet 10E: Robo-Batter

1.  Babe / Ty / Slim
$$\begin{array}{r} .335 \\ .347 \\ +.298 \\ \hline .980 \end{array}$$

2.  Ty / Joe
$$\begin{array}{r} .347 \\ -.198 \\ \hline .149 \end{array}$$

3.  .220    4.  .096    5.  .506

## Worksheet 10F: Decimal Dough Story Problems

| | | |
|---|---|---|
| 1a. $6.857 | 1b. eight | 1c. five |
| 1d. twenty | 2a. $96.84 | 2b. $0.8 or $0.80 |
| 2c. $0.04 | 2d. 84 hundredths | 2e. 3.16 |

## Worksheet 10G: Checkbook Problems

1.   150.00
2.   139.549   (150.00 – 10.451 = )
3.   343.620   (139.549        + 204.071 = )
4.   184.670   (343.620        – 158.950 = )
5.   369.340   (184.670        + 184.670 = )
6.   325.840   (369.340        – 43.500 = )
7.   321.290   (325.840        – 4.550 = )
8.   333.790   (321.290        – 12.500 = )

## Worksheet 10H: Kingdom of Wize Problems

1a.  Shrewd

1b.  Wiley

1c.  1,000.304 square miles        (1100.195 – 99.891 = )

2.   2,299.103 square miles        (1099.017 + 1100.195 + 99.891 = )

3.   1.178 square miles            (1100.195 – 1099.017 = )

4.   Shrewd

5.   $564,503.12                   ($9,564,002.11 – $8,999,498.99 = )

6.   4.646 inches of snow          (55.009 – 50.363 = )